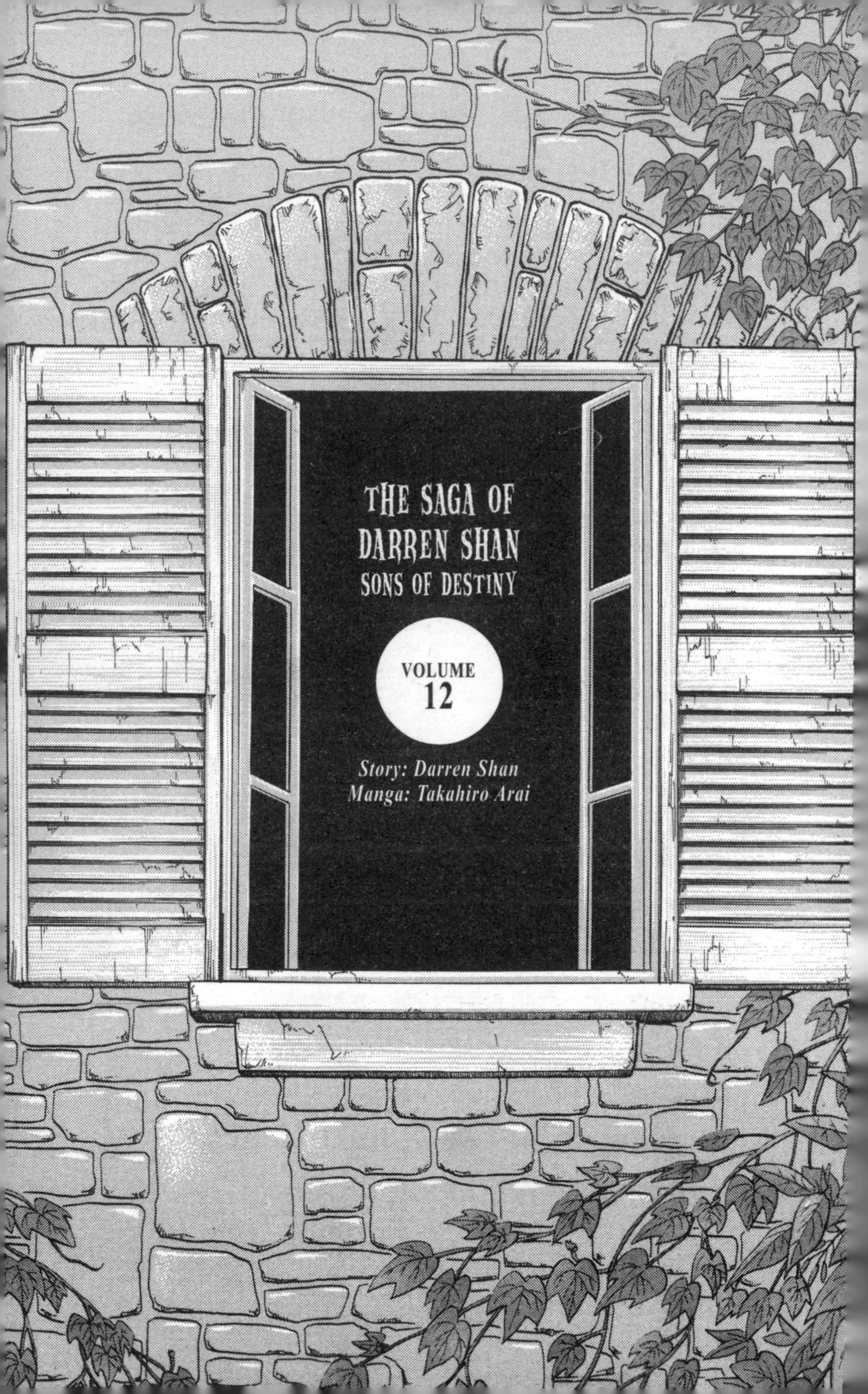
THE SAGA OF
DARREN SHAN
SONS OF DESTINY
VOLUME
12
Story: Darren Shan
Manga: Takahiro Arai

A SUMMARY OF LORD OF THE SHADOWS:

VISITING HIS HOMETOWN WITH THE CIRQUE DU FREAK, DARREN FALLS INTO A VAMPANEZE TRAP AND IS SHOT WITH A BOWGUN BY STEVE'S SON, DARIUS. SAVED BY THE VAMPIRITES, DARREN IS REUNITED WITH HIS FRIENDS, BUT ANOTHER ENEMY ATTACK LEADS TO EVRA'S SON, SHANCUS', ABDUCTION. WITH DARIUS HELD HOSTAGE IN ORDER TO STRIKE A DEAL, DARREN WITNESSES THE HORRIBLE SIGHT OF STEVE MURDERING SHANCUS. AND TO MAKE THINGS WORSE, DARIUS IS DARREN'S NEPHEW! EVEN GREATER TRAGEDY AWAITS!!

SONS OF DESTINY

CONTENTS

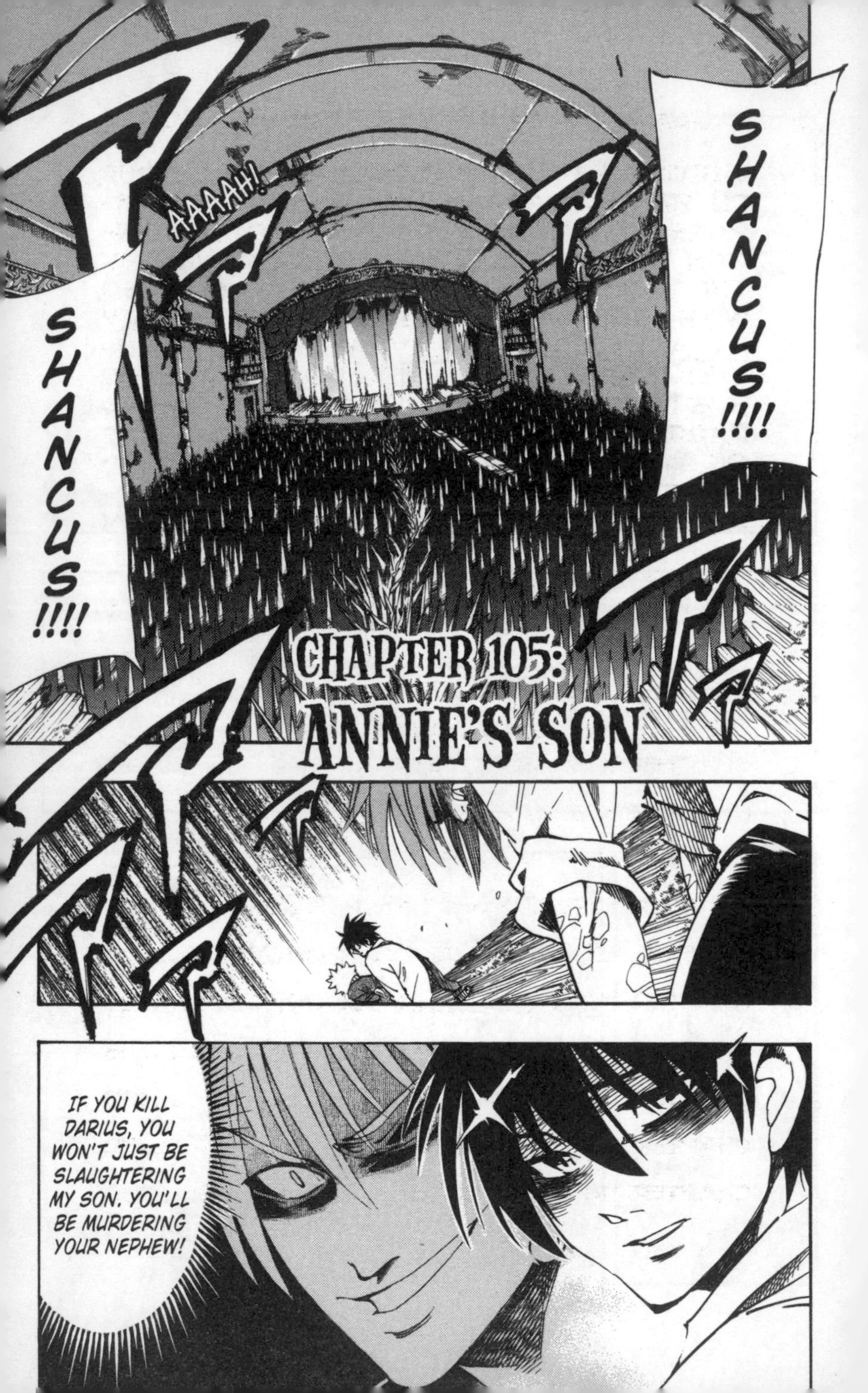
SHANCUS!!!!
AAAAH!
SHANCUS!!!!
CHAPTER 105: ANNIE'S SON
IF YOU KILL DARIUS, YOU WON'T JUST BE SLAUGHTERING MY SON. YOU'LL BE MURDERING YOUR NEPHEW!

SOB...
DARIUS IS THE SON OF ANNIE AND STEVE...
TRUE, HE DOES RESEMBLE ANNIE A BIT... BUT...
YOU'RE NOT THE BOY I SAW BEFORE ...
ANNIE WAS BRINGING IN LAUNDRY, BUT A CHUBBY BOY WITH BROWN HAIR LIKE HERS CAME OUT TO HELP HER...
THAT MUST HAVE BEEN OGGY BAS.
MY FRIEND. I SENT HIM OUT TO HELP MOM WITH THE LAUNDRY.
I RE-MEMBER THAT DAY...
DARIUS, LAUN-DRY!
SORRY, MOM. JUST A SEC...
OGGY, GO HELP HER!
......

I... DIDN'T KNOW ...
DAD TOLD ME VAMPIRES WERE EVIL. HE SAID YOU WERE MONSTERS.
AND THAT THE VAM-PANEZE WANTED TO STOP YOU FROM KILLING HUMANS ...

SORRY, FOLKS... I CHASED AFTER...
...BUT THEY'RE GONE. I LOST THEM.

AAAAH!
I WAS SO PROUD OF HIM FOR FIGHTING FOR HUMANITY. I WAS SO HAPPY TO BE HIS SON...
PORO (DRIP)
PORO
I'D HAVE DONE ANYTHING FOR HIM...
I HAD NO REASON TO DOUBT HIM.
I NEVER SAW HIM... LIKE I SAW HIM TONIGHT.
DOES ANNIE KNOW YOU WERE HELPING STEVE?
MY DAD IS... EVIL.

GO HOME. DON'T SPEAK TO STEVE AGAIN.
PUT THIS ALL BEHIND YOU.
NO, I NEVER TOLD HER I WAS MEETING HIM.
THEY HAVEN'T SPOKEN SINCE BEFORE I WAS BORN.
GOOD ...
SHURU (SLIP)
BE GOOD TO ANNIE, DARIUS.
MAKE HER HAPPY.
IT'S NOT THAT EASY.
GA (GRAB)
SOB ...

KUN (SNIFF)
KUN
KARI (SLICE)
!!
...AS I FEARED...
I DIDN'T NOTICE BECAUSE THERE WERE NO MARKS ON HIS FINGERS...
PERO (LICK)
HE'S BEEN BLOODED. VAMPANEZE BLOOD RUNS IN HIS VEINS.
ARE YOU SURE!?
WAS IT STEVE, DARIUS? DID HE DO THIS!?
IT'S THIN, BUT JUST ENOUGH TO KEEP HIM FROM RETURNING TO BEING A HUMAN.
DARIUS!!!

LET'S GO, SHAN-CUS...
BACK TO THE CIRQUE DU FREAK...
I'LL GO WITH EVRA...
ME TOO!
NO!
IF ANYTHING, WE SHOULD BE TRYING TO SAVE SHANCUS!
KEEP TRAILING R.V. TO WHEREVER HE'S HEADED.
IT'S MY FAULT. IT'S ALL MY FAULT...
WE'RE GOING TO STOP BY DARREN'S SISTER'S HOUSE.
PUT THIS ON.
ALONG THE WAY, WE CAN TEACH THIS LITTLE RUNT A THING OR TWO OF THE TRUTH ABOUT VAMPIRES AND VAMPANEZE.
...AS WELL AS WHAT IT MEANS TO HAVE VAMPANEZE BLOOD.

DO I REALLY HAVE TO DO THIS?
YES. IT'S FOR THE BOY'S SAKE.
IT WOULD BE WRONG TO RISK HIS LIFE WITHOUT INFORMING HIS MOTHER FIRST.
I KNOW BETTER THAN ANYONE HOW DANGEROUS THIS COULD BE...
UMM ...
C'MON, LET'S SEE YOUR MOM.
GACHA (CLICK)

EIGH-TEEN YEARS ...
EIGHTEEN YEARS SINCE THE LAST TIME I WAS HERE.
AND IT SEEMS LIKE IT'S BEEN EVEN LONGER...
MOM ...
I'M HOME.
THERE YOU ARE, DARIUS ...
DECIDED TO COME HOME AT LAST, DID YOU?
A ASHLE H
I WAS WORRIED. HAVE YOU SEEN THE NEWS? THERE'S—
コト
KOTO (TUNK)

OH...
IS THIS ONE OF YOUR FRIENDS ?

HELLO, ANNIE...
......
HAVE WE...MET BEFORE?
YOU KNEW ME A LONG TIME AGO.
EIGHTEEN YEARS AGO, IN FACT...
NONSENSE! YOU'D HAVE ONLY BEEN A BABY.
EIGHT... TEEN...
I'M SORRY, IS THIS A JOKE? YOU SHOULD PROBABLY LEAVE...
LOOK AT HIM, MOM. REALLY LOOK AT HIM!
QUIET, DARIUS!
I'LL BET YOU NEVER TOLD ANYONE ABOUT MADAM OCTA OR THE MAN IN RED, ANNIE.

NO...
I'M SORRY, ANNIE. YOU WERE SO YOUNG.
TOO YOUNG TO DEAL WITH THAT...
NO...
YORO (WOBBLE)
YOU CAN'T BE...
YES. I AM. IT'S ME, ANNIE.
DARREN.
LONG TIME NO SEE, SIS.
FURA (SWOON)
!!

I'M HOME ...
... ANNIE ...

I THINK I UNDERSTAND THE STORY OF THE VAMPIRES AND VAMPANEZE NOW...
BUT IT'S ALL SO SUD-DEN...
I CAN'T IMAGINE WHY YOU WOULD MAKE UP SOMETHING LIKE THIS... BUT IT'S SO HARD TO BELIEVE.
BUT MOM! EVERY-THING UNCLE DARREN SAYS IS TRUE!
TRUST ME!!
HE'S NOT YOUR UNCLE! DARREN IS DEAD!!
WE BURIED HIM EIGHTEEN YEARS AGO! HE'S DEAD AND THAT'S THAT!
SOB...
DARIUS!!
MOM...

STEVE LEONARD'S THE LORD OF THE VAMPANEZE...
PIKU (TWITCH)
HE CAME TO ME A FEW YEARS AGO. HE TOLD ME NOT TO SAY ANYTHING TO YOU.
HE SAID YOU WOULDN'T LIKE IT, THAT YOU'D MAKE HIM GO AWAY.
HE'S MY DAD. I THOUGHT HE LOVED ME...
THAT'S WHY I TRUSTED HIM.
HE SAID HE WAS TELLING ME FOR MY PROTECTION, THAT HE WAS WORRIED ABOUT ME—AND YOU.
HE WANTED TO PROTECT US. THAT'S WHEN I GOT MORE INVOLVED.
HE TAUGHT ME HOW TO USE A KNIFE, HOW TO SHOOT, HOW TO KILL.
HE GAVE ME A JOB TO DO: TO SPY ON THE CIRQUE DU FREAK, GET A TICKET FROM DARREN...
...AND GIVE THAT TICKET TO HIM.
IT WAS STEVE... STEVE WHO GOT ME INTO TROUBLE...
...WHO KILLED THE SNAKE-BOY, WHO MADE DARREN COME BACK TO SEE YOU.

DARREN DIDN'T WANT TO!
HE KNEW HE'D HURT YOU!
BUT STEVE LEFT HIM WITH NO CHOICE!
IT'S TRUE, MOM. EVERYTHING HE SAID. YOU'VE GOT TO BELIEVE US.
IT WAS STEVE, AND I THINK HE MIGHT COME BACK...
COME AFTER YOU, AND IF WE AREN'T READY...
...IF YOU DON'T BELIEVE ...
STEVE? WHAT DID I TELL YOU ABOUT HIM? I TOLD YOU NEVER TO GO NEAR HIM!
THAT IF YOU EVER SAW HIM, YOU HAD TO RUN AND TELL ME! I SAID HE WAS DANGEROUS!
BUT HE WAS MY DAD ...
I THOUGHT HE WOULD LOVE ME ...
HE WAS MY DAD...
I LOVED HIM...

ANNIE, NOW'S THE TIME...
...TO TELL YOU THE IMPORTANT STUFF.
STEVE BLOODED DARIUS, TRANSFERRING A SMALL AMOUNT OF HIS VAMPANEZE BLOOD TO HIM.
THE BLOOD WILL STRENGTHEN, HOWEVER.
HE CAN'T GO BACK TO BEING HUMAN.
AND IF WE DON'T DO ANYTHING ABOUT IT, HIS URGES FOR BLOOD WILL SOON CONSUME HIM.
THE ONLY WAY WE CAN SAVE HIM...
..IS TO SWAP MY BLOOD WITH HIS...

DARIUS HAS TO BECOME A VAMPIRE.
FIRST VAMPANEZE, NOW VAMPIRES!? NO! THERE MUST BE A BETTER WAY...
IF YOU DON'T WANT DARIUS TO BE A MURDERER, THIS IS THE ONLY ANSWER!!
BUT IT'S NOT CERTAIN. NOR IS IT SAFE.
IF IT FAILS...
...THE CELLS OF OUR OPPOSING BLOOD-LINES WILL BE POISON TO BOTH OF US.
I'LL DIE— AND SO WILL DARIUS.

CHAPTER 106: ANNIE'S DECISION

LISTEN UP, YOU TWO.
I'M GOING TO MEASURE THE TIME YOU NEED TO EXCHANGE BLOOD. JUST KEEP THE CONNECTION UNTIL YOU GET MY SAY-SO.
NEVER COULD HAVE GUESSED THAT MY EXPERIENCE BEING SAVED BY PARIS WOULD COME IN HANDY...
ARE YOU SURE YOU WANT TO DO THIS, DARREN?
I COULD JUST AS EASILY DO THE OPERATION.
MY VAMPIRE CELLS ARE HYPERACTIVE DUE TO MY SECOND PURGE. THEY MIGHT BE MORE EFFECTIVE IN DESTROYING THE VAMPANEZE CELLS.
ANYTHING TO GIVE US AN EDGE IN THE GAMBLE...
PLUS, I WANT TO BE THE ONE TO DO THIS.

AND THERE'S NO WAY TO RE-STORE HIS HU-MANITY?
DOCTORS, SURGERY, MEDICINE...
NO. THIS ISN'T A HUMAN DISEASE...
BUT IF YOU FAIL, AND BOTH YOU AND DARIUS DIE...
IT WOULD BE BETTER OR YOU TO DO OTHING AT ALL.
WOULD YOU RATHER LOSE HIM WHEN HE'S HUMAN...
...OR WHEN HE'S A KILLER LIKE HIS FATHER?
WE DON'T NEED TO USE THE TRADITIONAL FINGERTIP METHOD, DARIUS.
WE COULD USE SYRINGES...
NO. I'M DOING IT THE OLD WAY.

IF I'M GOING TO BE A VAMPIRE, I WANT TO BE A REAL ONE. I DON'T WANT TO HIDE MY MARKS.
IT'S ALL OR NOTHING.
ALL RIGHT.
SOUNDS LIKE YOU'VE MADE UP YOUR MIND.
BU (BLSHT)
!
GOOD. LET THEM BLEED ...
NOW HOLD UP YOUR HANDS ...
...AND PRESS YOUR TIPS TO MINE.

GIGYU (GLRRCH)
10!
I CAN FEEL THE VAMPANEZE BLOOD FLOWING INTO ME!!
15!
20!
25!
30!
THAT'S IT, DARIUS! HANG IN THERE!!
THAT'S IT! BREAK APART!!!

!!!!
DOO (THUD)
HAA (HUFF)
HAA
ARE YOU... ALL R—
DOKUN (BADUM)

!!!!
DON'T INTERFERE!! NATURE MUST TAKE ITS COURSE!!
—!!
MY BLOOD IS BOILING!!
IT'S LIKE MY SKIN IS BEING BURNED FROM THE INSIDE OUT!!!
MEGO (BLURP)
MEKO

PRESSURE BUILDING AT THE BACK OF MY EYE-SOCKETS!
IT'S LIKE MY BRAIN IS TRYING TO BULGE OUT OF MY HEAD!!
WAS IT A FAIL-URE !?
I'M DYING ...
DYING!
DYING!
I CAN'T STOP THE BLOOD!!
DARI-US...
DON'T DIE...
DARI ...

DAR-
REN!!
DARREN, WHY DID YOU DIE!?
DON'T LEAVE ME BY MYSELF, DAR-
REN!!
I DON'T WANT YOU TO GO!!
DARREN
!!!!

YOU'VE COME THROUGH IT. YOU'LL BE OKAY—WITH THE LUCK OF THE VAMPIRES.
DARI-US?
HE LOOKS SO SWEET WHEN HE'S ASLEEP.
YOU SHOULD HEAR THE THINGS HE SAYS ABOUT ME WHEN HE'S AWAKE...
HE MIGHT HAVE A FEW MORE CONVUL-SIONS...
...BUT VANCHA SAYS THE WORST IS OVER.
I DON'T KNOW HOW TO THANK YOU...
IF I'D LOST HIM, I DON'T KNOW WHAT I'D DO ...

WHEN I WAS A TEENAGER, I HAD A TOUGH TIME OF IT. WILD MOOD SWINGS, SELF-LOATHING...
STEVE CAME BACK TO TOWN IN THOSE YEARS.
HE WAS SO KIND AND PASSIONATE...
HE TREATED ME LIKE A REAL LADY.
WHEN I TOLD HIM I WAS PREGNANT, HE GOT THIS GLINT IN HIS EYE. I THOUGHT HE WAS OVERJOYED...
...BUT I WAS WRONG.
WHEN THE TIME CAME FOR DARIUS TO BE BORN, HE TURNED TO ME AND SAID...
"THERE'S NO TURNING BACK NOW."
BURU (SHIVER)
THEN HE LEFT TOWN, AND I HAVEN'T SEEN HIM SINCE.
GU (SQUEEZE)
BUT I'VE NO REGRETS...
STEVE MAY BE A TERRIBLE PERSON, BUT HE GAVE ME THE GREATEST GIFT IN THE WORLD.

I-I'M SORRY, HERE I AM, BLAB-BERING AWAY...
WOULD YOU LIKE SOME-THING TO DRINK? WATER?
NO, HE'S WEAK. AT A TIME LIKE THIS, HE NEEDS BLOOD.
BLOOD ...?
...
SU (SLIT)
ALICE ...
DRINK UP.
YOU LOOK AWFUL. YOU HAVEN'T HAD HUMAN BLOOD IN QUITE A WHILE, HAVE YOU?
YOU'RE SOME WOMAN, MISS BUR-GESS.
THE BEST.
YOU WANT SOME TOO, WHILE WE'RE AT IT?
...

WHAT HAPPENS NEXT?
FIRST, WE'RE SENDING ANNIE AND DARIUS OUT OF TOWN.
ALICE, GET IN TOUCH WITH THE VAMPIR-ITES AND VAMPIRES.
A VAMPIRE WILL LINK UP WITH THEM AND INSTRUCT DARIUS...
...OR GUIDE HIM TO VAMPIRE MOUN-TAIN, WHERE HE CAN BE LOOKED AFTER.
VAM-PIRE... MOUN-TAIN?
I'LL EX-PLAIN LATER. IT'S A SAFE PLACE.
WE'RE ALSO TAKING DARREN BACK TO THE CIRQUE TO RECOVER.
THE STADIUM'S NOT FAR FROM HERE.
WHAT WAS THAT ABOUT A STA-DIUM?
THE OLD SOCCER STADIUM AT THE EDGE OF TOWN?
YOU DIDN'T SEE TONIGHT'S NEWS!?
YOU NEED TO SEE THIS! IT MIGHT STILL BE ON!
There is a palpable sense of ten-sion in the air here!

I don't think I've ever seen so many armed officers in one place!
The stadium is entirely surround-ed!
The vicious killers who attacked Tommy Jones are still sheltering inside with their freakish crew...
...as police prepare to infilrate the stadium and taken them all down!!
LIVE
BCN
THEY'VE FRAMED THE CIRQUE DU FREAK FOR THE MURDER!! OH NO...
LOOK AT THE OFFICER BEHIND THE RE-PORTER.
A "V" TATTOO ON HIS TEMPLE.
HE'S A VAMPET ...

I CAN'T EXPLAIN IT, BUT I THINK STEVE'S THERE.
EVERYONE AT THE CIRQUE IS IN MORTAL PERIL...
YOU'VE GOT TO TAKE EVERY-THING YOU MIGHT NEED.
YOU MAY NOT BE ABLE TO COME BACK.
YOU REALLY CAN'T COME WITH US?
I CAN SEE SMOKE COMING FROM THE STADIUM. SOMETHING'S ALREADY GOING ON IN THERE.
EVEN KNOWING... IT'S A TRAP?
I'LL COME BACK TO FIND YOU ONCE EVERYTHING IS OVER...

YOU WILL?
YES ...
IN THE NEXT TWENTY-FOUR HOURS, EITHER YOU OR STEVE WILL BE THE LORD OF THE SHADOWS.
IF EVERY-THING GOES WELL...
...I'LL BE BACK.
MAKE SURE YOU GO TO THE ADDRESS ALICE GAVE YOU.
THE VAMPIRITES AND VAMPIRES YOU MEET THERE WILL HELP YOU.
I WISH I'D BEEN ABLE TO SAY GOOD-BYE TO DARIUS...
IT'S NOT GOOD-BYE.
JUST AU REVOIR.

I WISH YOU ALL THE LUCK IN THE WORLD.
AU RE-VOIR ...
...BIG BROTH-ER.
ARE YOU GOING TO BE ALL RIGHT?

SHE STILL CALLED ME...
..."BIG BROTHER" ...
THANKS. THIS WAS QUITE A DETOUR.
EVEN THOUGH I MAY NEVER SEE HER AGAIN ...
EVEN THOUGH ONLY DESPAIR WAITS AHEAD...
LET'S GO TO THE STADIUM.
...I HAVE NO CHOICE BUT TO KEEP MOVING ONWARD...
THE CIRQUE... AND STEVE... ARE WAITING!

CHAPTER 107: KINDRED

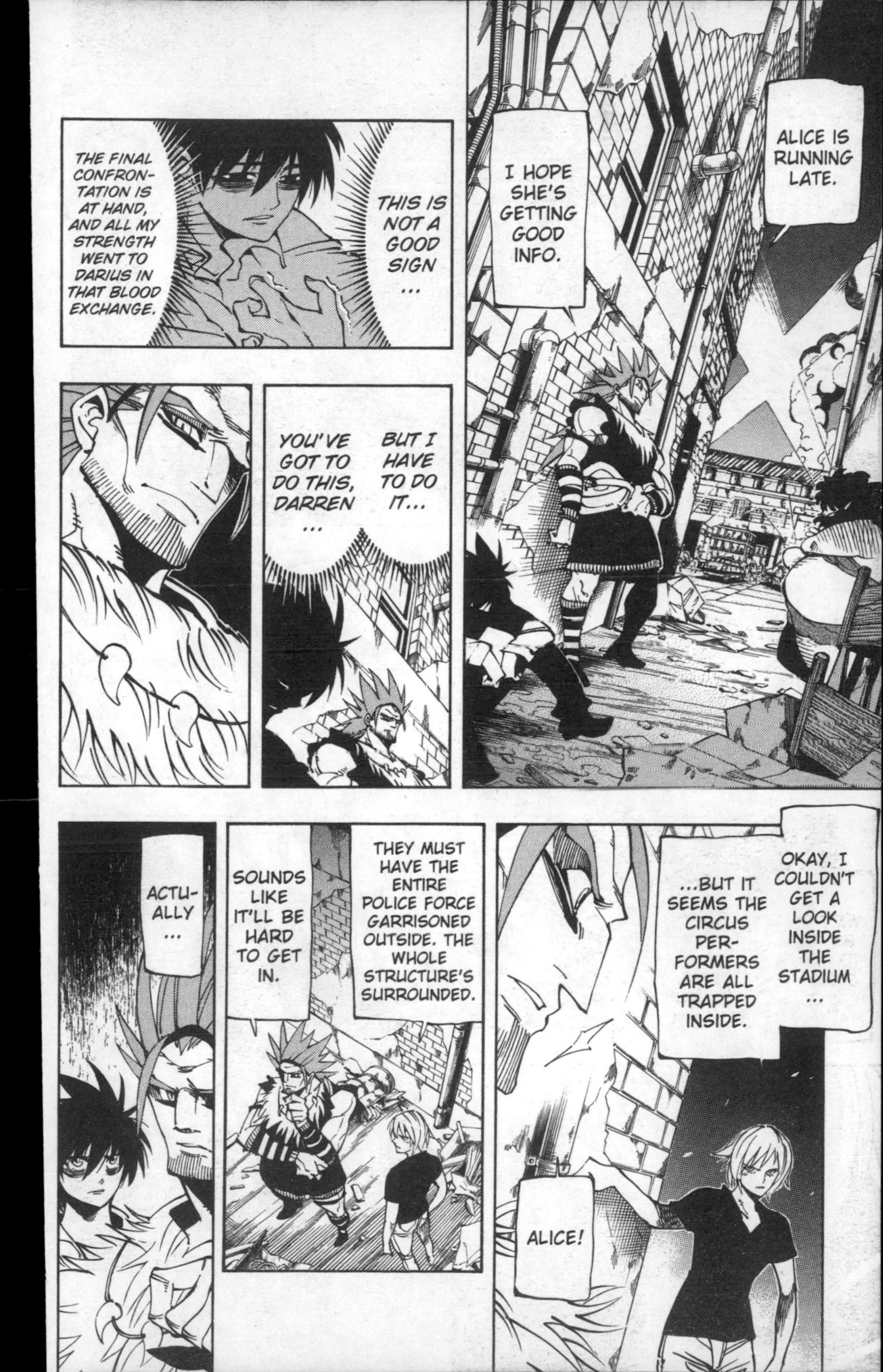
ALICE IS RUNNING LATE.
I HOPE SHE'S GETTING GOOD INFO.
THIS IS NOT A GOOD SIGN ...
THE FINAL CONFRONTATION IS AT HAND, AND ALL MY STRENGTH WENT TO DARIUS IN THAT BLOOD EXCHANGE.
BUT I HAVE TO DO IT...
YOU'VE GOT TO DO THIS, DARREN ...
OKAY, I COULDN'T GET A LOOK INSIDE THE STADIUM ...
...BUT IT SEEMS THE CIRCUS PERFORMERS ARE ALL TRAPPED INSIDE.
ALICE!
THEY MUST HAVE THE ENTIRE POLICE FORCE GARRISONED OUTSIDE. THE WHOLE STRUCTURE'S SURROUNDED.
SOUNDS LIKE IT'LL BE HARD TO GET IN.
ACTUALLY ...

East Stand
Gates 2469
Gates 1
NO OFFICERS HAVE BEEN TOLD EXPLIC-ITLY...
...BUT IT SEEMS THEY'RE NOT TO INTER-FERE WITH ANYONE AT THIS BACK ENTRANCE.
THIS IS CLEARLY SOME KIND OF SET-UP.
THE VAMPETS ARE PULLING THE STRINGS.
I WONDER WHAT THIS MEANS...
THEY REALLY ARE TURNING A BLIND EYE.
WE WON'T BE ABLE TO PUNCH OUR WAY OUT.
IF WE ALL GO IN, THEY'LL CLOSE THE NET AROUND US.
WAIT!
NOTHING STEVE DOES...
...WILL SURPRISE ME AT THIS POINT. LET'S GO!
I'VE GOT A BETTER IDEA...

Gate
EXIT
I'M GONNA LEAVE YOU IN CHARGE OF WHAT ALICE LEFT WITH US, DARREN.
YEAH, DON'T WOR-RY.
GASHA (CRUNCH)
GASHA
HMPH!
GASHA
GASHA
IT'S LIKE WE'RE GOING RIGHT INTO THE LEOP-ARD'S DEN.
...
BE-TWEEN ME, VANCHA AND STEVE ...
...ONE OF US WILL DIE TONIGHT.
IF VANCHA OR I DIE, STEVE BECOMES THE LORD OF THE SHADOWS AND RULES THE WORLD.
IF STEVE DIES, I BECOME THE LORD, DESTROY MY FRIEND VANCHA, AND LAY WASTE TO THE WORLD.
IS THERE NO OTHER FUTURE BEYOND THESE CHOICES?
CAN THERE BE... NO OTHER POSSIBILI-TIES?

GOOOOOOO
(FWOOOM)
CIRCU

I MAKE IT A DOZEN-PLUS VAMPANEZE ...
HISO (WHISPER)
...AND THREE TIMES THAT NUMBER OF VAMPETS, AYE?
THE ODDS ARE IN OUR FAVOR ...
...SIRE.
IT'S ONLY THEIR LORD WHO CAN FINISH OFF THE HUNTERS.
WE JUST HAVE TO BEAT STEVE, AND IT'S ALL OVER.

I HATE YOU...
GA (GRAB)
!!
MY SON IS DEAD BECAUSE OF YOU !!!
MERLA, I'M SORRY...I WOULDN'T... I DIDN'T...
IF I COULD ...
NO, LEAVE THEM ALONE !!
THIS IS FUN ...

DON (WHAM)
IT'S YOUR FAULT!!
DO (WHAM)
IT'S YOUR FAULT!!!
I'LL KILL YOU!!
POTA (DRIP)
YOU DE-SERVE TO DIE!
NIYA NIYA (SMIRK)
OH, MERLA...
THAT'S IT, STRON-GER...
GUGU (URRG)
SQUEEZE HARDER...
IT WASN'T YOUR FAULT.

WE DON'T HATE YOU.
STEVE'S THE EVIL ONE—NOT YOU.
HA HA HA!
WE DIDN'T FIGHT.
THEY THINK WE'RE GUT-LESS...
...BUT WE WERE WAITING FOR YOU.
HARKAT SAID YOU'D COME...
...AND SAVE US.
GIVE US A SIGNAL WHEN YOU'RE READY, AND WE'LL ANSWER THE CALL.
WE'LL FIGHT TO THE DEATH, EVERY LAST ONE OF US.

I'LL KILL YOU ... YOU DEVIL ...
BURU
BURU (SHIVER)
MOM ...
YOU OKAY DARREN?
BOSO (MUTTER)
THEY'RE WITH US.
THEY'LL FIGHT WHEN WE DO.

STOP RIGHT THERE.
BASA (FLAP)
DO NOT APPROACH ANY CLOSER.
WHY DO YOU GO ALONG WITH THIS MADMAN, GANNEN?
I'M CONTENT TO SERVE AND PROTECT, IN LINE WITH THE WISHES OF THOSE WHO APPOINTED ME.
AM I WRONG, BROTH-ER?
IT'S A SAD LIFE ...

BROTHERS SPLIT BY LOYALTIES. HOW HEARTRENDING.
SPEAKING OF WHICH, WE'RE NOW BROTHERS-IN-LAW, AREN'T WE, DARREN?
I WAS HOPING YOU'D BRING ANNIE AND DARIUS ALONG.
AREN'T FAMILY GET-TOGETHERS A JOY?
THEY'RE FAR AWAY FROM HERE BY NOW.
DARIUS UNDERSTANDS THE TRUTH NOW.
YOU'VE LOST HIM. HE'S YOUR SON NO MORE.
OH WELL, I WAS NEVER THAT FOND OF HIM ANYWAY.
A SCRAWNY, MOODY KID NO TASTE FOR BLOOD.
HEH HEH
ALTHOUGH I GUESS HE'LL DEVELOP ONE SOON...
I'LL BET YOU NEVER NOTICED THAT I BLOODED HIM.
HE'S HALF-VAMPANEZE!
DIKU (TWITCH)
I DID KNOW.
BUT HE'S NOT ANYMORE...

NOW HE'S A HALF-VAMPIRE. LIKE ME.
YOU...RE-BLOODED HIM?
YOU SHOULDN'T HAVE DONE THAT! THE BOY WAS MINE!!!
I'VE CHANGED MY MIND! I WAS GOING TO STRIKE A DEAL WITH YOU, BUT NOT ANYMORE!!
GASHA (CRUNCH)
R.V.! RIP THAT WOMAN'S GUTS OUT AND SHOW DARREN WHAT HIS STUPIDITY HAS BROUGHT ABOUT!!
R.V.! DIDN'T YOU HEAR ME!?
KILL HER!!!
DON'T WANT TO...
YOU SHOULDN'T HAVE... KILLED THE KID, STEVE...
SAM... OH, SAM. POOR KID SHOULDN'T HAVE DIED...
HE WAS TOO YOUNG... KIDS ARE THE FUTURE...
IF I HADN'T OPENED THAT CAGE...
KACHA (CLINK)
THAT SNAKE-BOY SHOULDN'T HAVE DIED. IT WASN'T WHAT YOU SAID...
KACHA
WHAT ABOUT MY HANDS? WHERE... WHERE DID SAM GO?
WHAT HE HELL ARE YOU BLATHERING ABOUT?

STOP SPUTTERING AND KILL HER!!!
I GAVE YOU AN ORDER, AND YOU'LL OBEY IT!!
PIKU (TWITCH)
YOU POOR, SAD MAN...
YOU DON'T REALIZE THAT NO ONE WILL LOVE YOU FOR THIS...
YOU CAN ONLY FORM A CONNECTION TO OTHERS THROUGH PAIN AND CONTROL.
I'M SO... SICK...
HEH HEH...
HA HA HA HA!
YORO (WOBBLE)
...OF EVERYONE TRYING TO RUIN MY PERFECT PLAN...
I FOLLOWED TINY'S PROPHECY, SET UP THE PERFECT STAGE FOR OUR FINAL CONFRONTATION...
...AND THIS IS HOW YOU CHOOSE TO REPAY MY FAITHFULNESS?
DON'T YOU GET IT, DARREN?
IT'S TONIGHT! THE NIGHT WHEN ALL OF OUR FATES ARE MADE CLEAR!!
GASHAA (CRAAASH)

GOO
(WHOOSH)
I BE-
LIEVE
...
...IN NO
PROPH-
ECY.

HOW CAN YOU NOT!? DESMOND TINY IS THE VOICE OF DESTINY!
HE SEES THE FUTURE! HE KNOWS ALL THAT HAS BEEN AND WILL BE!
OPEN YOUR EYES! UNPLUG YOUR EARS!!
ACCEPT THE PROPHECY, DARREN!!!
"DESTINY"? "PROPH-ECY"?
NO. THESE THINGS ARE NOTHING BUT "WORDS."
GACHA (CLICK)
!!
YOU'RE THE ONE UNDER THE SWAY OF MEAN-INGLESS WORDS...
GU (CHUNCH)
GUGU
...YOU'RE THE ONE WHO'S BLIND TO REALITY, STEVE.

DAAN (BLAM)
WHAT'S REALLY IMPORTANT IS WHAT YOU THINK AND THE CHOICES YOU MAKE!!
MEANING —!
POINT YOUR GUN IN THE AIR AND FIRE THREE TIMES.
THAT'S THE SIGNAL TO TTACK!
DAAN
THAT THE UTURE IS OMETHING E CREATE WITH OUR OWN HANDS!!!

DAAN (BLAM)
THERE'S THE SIGNAL !!!
OO (RAHH)
WE'RE GOING IN!!!
SUR-ROUND OUR LORD !!!!
HE MUST BE PROTECT-ED!!!!

CHAPTER 108:
A MAN'S DEATH

WHAT'S GOING ON I THOUGH THEY WERE AL COWARDS TERRIFIE OF US!!
BACK, MY LORD!!
ZUBAA (CHARGE)
STEVE!!!
HARKAT!
DAR-REN! YOU'RE HERE!!
GIN (CLANG)

DEBBIE!!
TRUSKA!!
YOU'RE HURT!
IT NOT SO BAD...
I NEED ASK YOU SOMETHING, DEBBIE.
......
AAGH!!!
BARARA (SLICE)

MUNYU
MUNYU SPROUT
KEEP DOING THAT. IT WON'T DO YOU ANY GOOD ...
URGH...
I CAN'T TAKE IT, MAN... JUST LET ME GO...
I DON'T WANT TO FIGHT!
THE DEVIL YOU DON'T, YOU BIG, BEARDED, BUG-EYED BABOON!!
YOU'LL HAVE TO DO BETTER THAN THAT, STINK-BREATH!!
THEN I WILL !!!!

I DIDN'T WANT TO KILL ANY-BODY!
I WANTED TO HELP PEOPLE. I WANTED TO SAVE THE WORLD ...
PIKU (TWITCH)
YOU SHOULDN'T HAVE MESSED WITH ME, MAN!!
SOB ...
WHY... WHY ME?
WHAT DID I DO TO DESERVE THIS?
I SEE!
NYOKI (SPROUT)
NYOKI
SO THAT'S WHAT HAPPENS WHEN MY HEAD GETS CUT OFF!
I ALWAYS WON-DERED ABOUT THAT!

HA HA!
HA HA HA!
MADNESS! THE WORLD'S GONE MAD!
MAD!!!
HERE WE GO.
IT'S TIME, BOYS.
DA (DASH)
DARREN!!
STEVE AND GANNEN WENT OUTSIDE!!
TO THE DEATH, SIRE?
TO THE DEATH.

SCALY EVRA VON...
GREY-SKINNED HARKAT MULDS...
STEELY ALICE BURGESS...
THE REST OF THE CIRQUE DU FREAK...
YOU SHOULD NEVER HAVE BEEN DRAGGED INTO THIS TERRIBLE WAR...
THIS MEANS MORE THAN I CAN EVER SAY.
DARREN.
DEBBIE.
TRUSKA GAVE THIS TO ME.
ISN'T THAT MR. CREPSLEY'S ...?
I WISH I COULD GO WITH YOU, BUT I'D ONLY HOLD YOU BACK.
YOU FOCUS ON STOPPING STEVE, AND I'LL LEAD THE RESCUE.

I'LL SEE YOU SOON ...
GOOD-BYE, EVERYONE...
GOOD-BYE, MY BELOVED DEBBIE HEMLOCK...
... DARREN.

ENOUGH! STOP HERE!
BUT ...
GAN-NEN!!
WE FIGHT BACK HERE ...

GREET-INGS, BROTHER.
GREETINGS. I'M GLAD YOU FACE US LIKE TRUE CREATURES OF THE NIGHT AT LAST.
PERHAPS IN DEATH YOU CAN FIND AGAIN...
...THE HONOR THAT YOU ABANDONED DURING LIFE.
HONOR WILL BE SHARED BY ALL HERE TONIGHT, BOTH THE LIVING AND THE DEAD.
THEY LOVE TALK-ING...
WELL, SHAN?
READY TO DIE?
IF THAT'S WHAT FATE HAS IN STORE FOR ME—YES.
BUT I'M ALSO READY TO KILL.

GUI (YANK)
DARREN!!!
GA (GRAB)
BOGI (CRUNCH)
DO (THUD)

ZUDA (THWAM)
MUST BE TOUGH, GANNEN ...
... TRAPPED BETWEEN YOUR BELIEFS AND YOUR DUTY.
ALLOW ME TO FREE YOU FROM YOUR SUFFER-ING!!
PASHI (SNIK)

DO (SHKK)
GAHA (GAHK)
VANCHA!!!
GAAAAAAAAAAHHH!!!!
BAKI (CRAK)
YOU'LL COME LAST.
YOU STAY THERE AND WATCH YOUR FRIEND DIE.
HURRY! KILL HIM QUICK!
BEFORE HE DIES OF THE WOUND I GAVE HIM!!
PA-TIENCE, PA-TIENCE...

YOU HESITATED... AGAIN...
YOU CHOSE YOUR BROTHER'S LIFE OVER THE FUTURE OF YOUR PEOPLE...
YOU AREN'T WORTHY OF BEING A LEADER...
EVEN IN THE END, YOU DON'T KNOW...
...WHERE YOUR OWN PRIORITIES LIE...

NOT GONNA LET YOU DO IT, MAN!!
ZUBA (SWOOSH)
YOU'RE EVIL ...!!
FURA (WOBBLE)
FURA
GAKU (SLUMP)
BURU (TREMBLE)
BURU

MY HANDS ...
EVERY-THING'S OKAY NOW...
GOPO (BLURP)
I'M...
I CAN SEE THEM... MY HANDS, THEY'RE BACK...
... NORMAL ...
... AGAIN ...

HA (CHUFF)
HA
ZE (WHEEZE)
ZE

KACHI (TICK)
GANNEN'S DOWN...
KACHI
...AND VANCHA'S DOWN AS WELL.
KACHI
WE HAD A LITTLE SURPRISE ...
CHAPTER 109: THE FINAL CONFRONTATION
SOON, ALL WILL BE DECIDED.
VERY SOON...

CHAPTER 109:
THE FINAL CONFRONTATION

VANCHA'S STILL BREATHING, BUT HE DOESN'T HAVE MUCH TIME LEFT...
HA
HA (HUF)
URGH...
YOU'RE A MESS, DARREN...
BLOODING DARIUS LEFT YOU A SHAMBLING WRECK.
ON TOP OF THAT, YOUR LEFT ARM IS COMPLETELY USELESS NOW...
WHAT ABOUT YOU? CAN YOU FIGHT WITHOUT GANNEN TO DO IT FOR YOU?
I'LL TAKE THIS.
I...AM SORRY... MY... LORD...
ENOUGH...
REST. YOU FULFILLED YOUR DUTY.

I HAD A FEELING IT WOULD COME DOWN TO JUST THE TWO OF US IN THE END.
IN FACT, I THINK I ALWAYS KNEW IT WOULD WIND UP THIS WAY...
IT'S ONLY NATURAL... YOU AND I ARE TWO SIDES OF THE SAME COIN.
WE HAVE ALWAYS BEEN BOUND—BY FRIEND-SHIP AS CHILDREN, AND BY HATRED AFTER THAT.
OUR EIGHTEEN-YEAR SCORE IS SETTLED HERE!
YES, THE TIME IS AT HAND.

GIIN
(CLAANG)
OHO!!
FLIT.
FLIT.
FLIT
AGAIN
...

SUCH A CRISP TRAD-ING OF FLITTING BLOWS ...
A MOST AGILE BATTLE ...
VAM-PIRES AND VAM-PANEZE ...
FU (FZZ)
SUCH FASCI-NATING CREA-TURES.

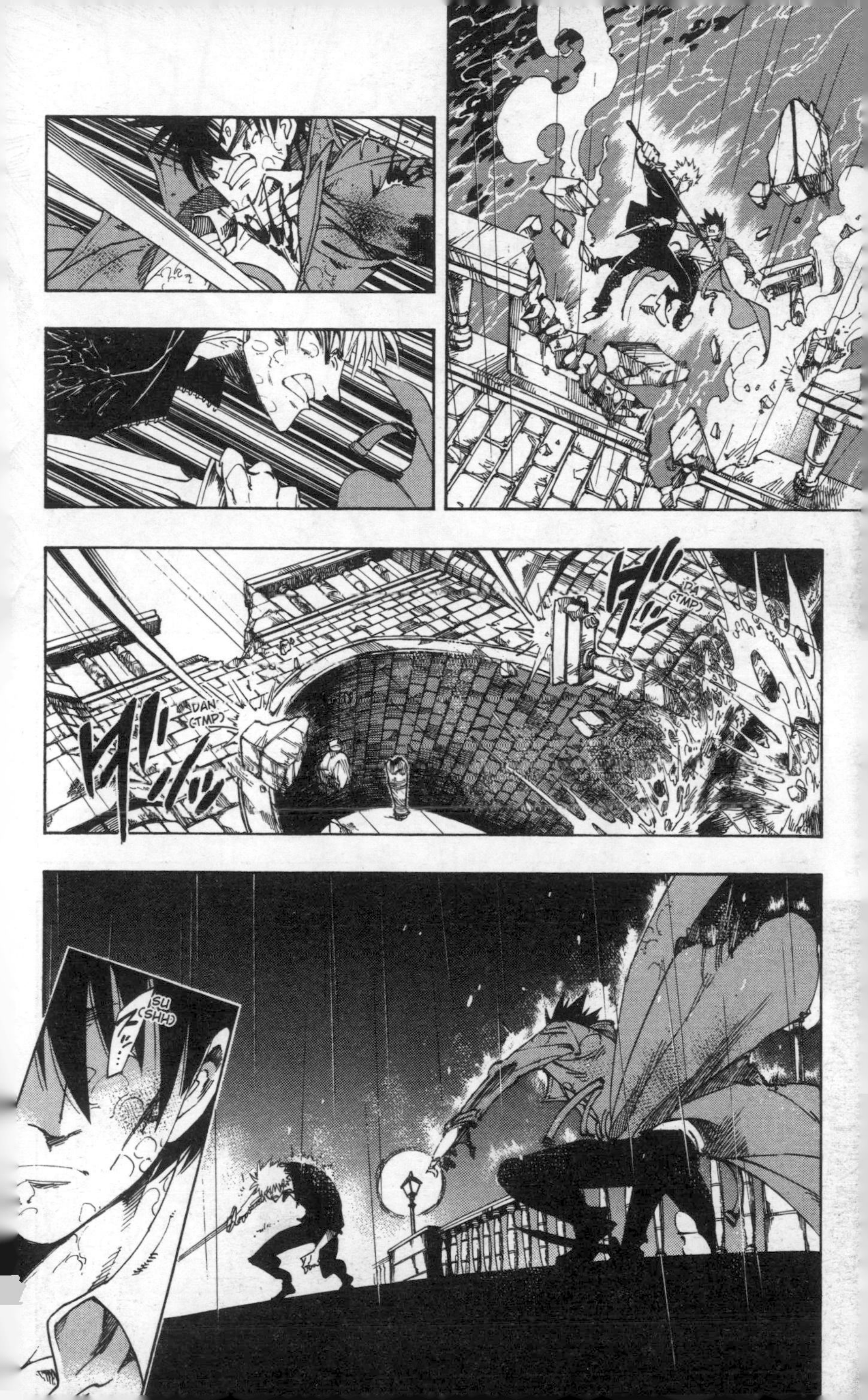
DA (TMP)
DAN (TMP)
SU (SHH)

HAVE I EVER TOLD YOU...
...HOW MUCH I HATE YOU?
STEVE... YOUR EYES...
BA (SLAP)
ARE YOU ...
... UNDER-GOING THE PURGE TOO?
REMEMBER THE NIGHT I DID THIS TO MY HAND?

THAT NIGHT, I PROMISED VEN-GEANCE.
I SWORE I'D KILL YOU AND CREEPY CREPSLEY.
YOU'RE HALFWAY THERE.
YOU MUST BE DE-LIGHT-ED.
NOT REALLY. TO BE HONEST, I MISS OLD CREEPY.
THE WORLD'S NOT THE SAME WITHOUT HIM.
AND ONCE YOU'RE DEAD...
GORO (RUMBLE)
GORO
...I'LL MISS YOU EVEN MORE.
YOU'VE BEEN THE DRIVING FORCE BEHIND EVERY-THING I'VE DONE SINCE I WAS A CHILD.
WITHOUT YOU, I'M NOT SURE I'LL HAVE MUCH OF AN INTEREST IN LIFE.
IF POSSIBLE, I'D LET YOU GO. I ENJOY OUR GAMES...
...THE HUNT, THE TRAPS, THE FIGHTS. I'D HAPPILY KEEP DOING IT, OVER AND OVER.

I'LL DO THAT LATER.
HERE'S WHERE YOU END, DARREN SHAN.
HAVE YOU MADE YOUR PEACE WITH THE VAMPIRE GODS?
YES. THAT'S ONE THING I CAN'T CHANGE ...
BUT LIFE DOESN'T WORK LIKE THAT. EVERY-THING HAS TO END.
GIN (CLING)
GYARI (SHHING)

GAKAA
(FLAASH)

GOPO (BLORP)
DOSHA (SLUMP)
URGH ...
HAA (HUFF)
HAA
I'VE GOT YOU NOW!!
GUSA (STOMP)
GOT YOU !!!
GUSA
I'VE GOT YOU!!

!!!
AND WHEN I FINISH CUTTING OFF YOUR TOES AND FINGERS ...
!!!
...I'LL MOVE ON TO YOUR NOSE AND EARS!!!
!!
!!
I CAN FEEL MY LIFE... EBBING AWAY, BIT BY BIT...
SO... I'VE LOST ...
I'M SORRY... VANCHA ...
I CAN SEE FACES. SO MANY FACES ...
THE FACES OF THOSE WHO DIED BEFORE ME...

IN THE END...THE BURDEN WAS TOO MUCH FOR ME TO BEAR...
TOO MUCH... WITHOUT MR. CREPSLEY AT MY SIDE...
I HAD HOPED THAT... WEARING YOUR COAT...
...WOULD MAKE ME STRONG LIKE YOU...
BUT IT'S NOT...THAT EASY... IN REAL LIFE...
SUU (SHHH)
!!
...BLEED!
AFTER THAT...
IT'S SO... STRANGE ...
THE SMELL OF THE BLOOD... SOAKED INTO THIS COAT...RE-ASSURES ME...

THE SMELL OF EIGHTEEN YEARS' TRAVEL.
THE VAMPIRE BLOOD AND VAMPIRE PRIDE...YOU LEFT WITH ME...
...STILL LIVES ON, INSIDE ...
THAT'S RIGHT...MR. CREPSLEY'S ALWAYS BEEN...WITH ME...
PIKU (TWITCH)
I'M...
...NOT... ALONE...

FIRST I'LL CUT YOUR EYELIDS OFF..
...SO YOU CAN SEE EVERY-THING THAT I'M GONNA DO!!
AFTER THAT...
STE... VE...
WANT TO KNOW...THE SECRET OF... WINNING A FIGHT LIKE THIS...?
BIKI (CRAK)
BIKI
VAM-PIRE BLOOD ... ...AND VAMPIRE PRIDE ...
LESS TALKING.
...GRANT ME STRENGTH !!
MORE STAB-BING !!!

OH...
SUCH A PITIFUL HEART...
DO (THUD)
GURA (SLUMP)

YORO (WOBBLE)
KAH...
GOPO (BLUPP)
HRRK!
STEVE...
WHAT PASSION! WHAT VALOR!
PACHI (CLAP)
PACHI
WHAT A NEVER-SAY-DIE SPIRIT!!
IT COULD HAVE GONE EITHER WAY, BUT IF I WERE A BETTING MAN, I'D HAVE BET BIG ON YOU.
PACHI
PACHI
I SAID AS MUCH BEFORE-HAND, DIDN'T I, EVANNA?
PACHI
YES, FATHER.

THE VAMPANEZE WILL FALL, AND SO SHALL THE HUMANS.
THIS WORLD WILL BE YOURS, DARREN. RATHER, OURS!!
COME, DARREN. FINISH STEVE OFF!
WE MUST HAVE YOUR WOUNDS SEEN TO...
MUCH WILL COME IN TIME, MY BOY!!
TOGETHER WE'LL BUILD A WORLD OF CHAOS AND TWISTED BEAUTY!
YOUR HAND AT THE TILLER, MY VOICE IN YOUR EAR.
YOU WILL ACCEPT ME, DARREN. YOU WERE BORN TO.
BLOOD IS THICKER THAN WATER, MY BOY.
WHAT MAKES YOU THINK...
...I'D HAVE ANYTHING TO DO... WITH A MONSTER LIKE YOU?

LIKE SIDES WITH LIKE.
SON SIDES WITH FATHER.
COME AND GIVE YOUR FATHER A HUG, DAR-REN— MY SON !!!

WHAT IN THE WORLD IS HE TALKING ABOUT...?
I'M... YOUR...

...SON?
CHAPTER 110: CHILDREN OF DESTINY
THAT CAN'T BE TRUE!!!
THAT'S RIGHT. BASK IN YOUR FATHER'S LOVE...
...DAR-REN.

YOU'RE INSANE!! I HAVE A FATHER: DERMOT SHAN!
NOT YOU!!!
DOKU DOKU (BLUB)
ドクドク
URGH...
I AM NOT A LIAR...
NOW, FINISH OFF STEVE FOR GOOD.
YOU ARE THE LORD OF THE SHADOWS.
WHAT DOES THIS MEAN? YOU ARE HIS FATHER? HAVE YOU TWISTED THE STRANDS OF FATE TO ACHIEVE THIS END!?
YOU MUST BE PLEASED, DEAR DAUGHTER. YES, YOU HAVE A NEW BROTHER.
EVANNA, HIBERNIUS...
YOU WERE FASCINATING AT FIRST, BUT I GREW TIRED OF YOUR LIMITATIONS.

I DID MY BEST, NUDGING NATIONS ALONG THE PATH TO BATTLE, PUTTING TYRANTS AND DICTATORS INTO POWER ...
BUT I FOUND A WAY TO STRETCH—BUT NOT BREAK—THE RULES TO BRING CHAOS INTO THE PICTURE.
BECAUSE YOU CAN SEE INTO THE FUTURE, YOU—LIKE ME—ARE LIMITED IN WHAT YOU CAN DO IN THE PRESENT.
ALL OF US HAVE TO ABIDE BY LAWS NOT OF OUR MAKING.
BUT MORTALS ARE CONTRARY CREATURES AND SHORT-LIVED!
IT'S DIFFICULT TO MANIPULATE LARGE GROUPS OF HUMANS OVER A LONG PERIOD OF TIME...
...ESPECIALLY NOW THAT THERE ARE BILLIONS OF THEM.
WHAT I LONGED FOR WAS A MORTAL I COULD CHANNEL MY WILL THROUGH...
...A BEING NOT BOUND BY THE LAWS OF THE UNIVERSE, NOR SHACKLED BY THE CONFINES OF HUMANITY.
DO YOU UNDERSTAND THE PRECISION THIS PLAN DEMANDED? FAILURE WAS NOT AN OPTION.
MY ALLY WOULD HAVE TO START AS A HUMAN, THEN BECOME A VAMPIRE OR VAMPANEZE, LEADING HIS CLAN TO RULE OVER ALL...
...AND THROUGH HIS CHILDREN, I COULD CONTROL THE WORLD FOR THE REST OF TIME ITSELF!
TO WEED OUT ANY WEAKNESSES, I CREATED A PAIR OF HEIRS, THEN SET THEM AGAINST EACH OTHER.

A PAIR ...?
YOU MEAN ...
... STEVE ?
DARREN, YOU AND STEVE WERE CUCKOO'S CHILDREN, RAISED IN A NEST NOT YOUR OWN.
I DID MY WORK QUIETLY, UNKNOWN TO YOUR MOTHERS.
BUT TRUST ME...
...YOU ARE BOTH MINE!!!

THAT...
THAT CAN'T BE...
THIS IS OUTRAGEOUS...
ZAWA (MURMUR)
ZAWA
HOW DARE YOU, FATHER!!!
SHIRI (SWISH)
YOU HAVE TAMPERED WITH THE LAWS OF FATE!!!?
DO NOT DO THIS, EVANNA.
I HAVE NO DESIRE TO HARM MY OWN DAUGHTER.
SU (SWISH)

SHIJI (SZZZT)
GUH ...
GIJI (GRRK)
AGH ...
SHISHI (FSSK)
HOW DARE I?
NO, I SUPPOSE YOU WOULD NOT UNDER-STAND—YOU DEDICATE YOURSELF TO OBSERV-ING, NEVER ACTING.
IT IS FORBIDDEN, FATHER... THIS IS UNJUST.
THE UNIVERSE WILL PUNISH YOU FOR YOUR UNJUST MEDDLING! YOU HAVE RUINED THEIR LIVES!!
DOSA (THUDD)

RUINED!? WITH MY HELP, DARREN BECAME A PRINCE OF VAMPIRES ...
...AND STEVE A LORD OF VAMPANEZE!!
WHO WAS WHISPERING INTO DARREN'S EAR WHEN TO GRAB THAT TICKET ...
A SPIDER WHISPERED TO ME.
CLOSE YOUR EYES.
NOW !!
...ON THAT FATEFUL DAY, EIGHTEEN YEARS AGO!?
AND WHO WAS IT THAT PLANTED THAT SEED OF HATRED WITHIN STEVE...
...TOWARD DARREN AND LARTEN CREPSLEY AFTER THEIR FIRST MEETING !?
WHO INFLUENCED CREPSLEY AND INSPIRED HIM TO BLOOD DARREN!?
WHY I DID IT IS A LONG STORY ...
WHO URGED GANNEN HARST TO SUGGEST STEVE TRY THE COFFIN OF FIRE!?
IT WAS ME— ALL ME!!
BOTH OF YOU HAVE ENJOYED ENORMOUS SLICES OF GOOD FORTUNE IN LIFE, BUT IT WAS NEITHER THE LUCK OR SURVIVAL INSTINCT OF YOUR PEOPLE.
YOU OWE YOUR NINE CAT'S LIVES— AND QUITE A FEW MORE— TO ME!!

IT'S NOT TRUE!! IT'S NOT TRUE, IT'S NOT TRUE!!
OH, BUT IT IS!!
SHUT UP! IT'S BULL, ALL OF IT!!
YOU'RE NOT MY FATHER!! YOU'RE A MON-STER!!!
THAT'S RIGHT!!!
AND SO ARE YOU!!!
YOU'VE DONE ENOUGH... YOU'VE FOUGHT AND SUFFERED YOUR SHARE...
NOW ACCEPT YOUR DESTINY. YOU ARE THE LORD OF THE SHADOWS...
GIVE IN. DON'T RESIST.
MON-STERS HAVE ALL THE FUN, MY BOY.

THE TEARS... WON'T STOP COMING ...
ALL OF MY BATTLES... EVERYTHING I'VE DONE ...
... WASN'T FOR MY FRIENDS AND LOVED ONES ...
...BUT FOR THE SAKE OF MR. TINY...?
F- FA...
FA- THER ...
HELP... ME...
POTA (DRIP)

I NEVER... HAD A... DAD...
I... WANT... TO KNOW... YOU...
I'LL... SERVE... YOU...
...AND... LOVE... YOU...
WHAT ON EARTH WOULD I WANT WITH LOVE!?
SERVITUDE, GRATITUDE, FEAR, HATRED, ANGER—THESE I LIKE.
BUT... I'M...
...YOUR... SON...
YOU CAN TAKE YOUR LOVE TO THE LAKE OF SOULS WHEN YOU DIE!!
YOU WERE. NOW YOU'RE JUST A LOSER.
THIS IS A WINNER'S WORLD. DAR-REN'S MY ONLY SON NOW.
I'LL TOSS YOUR CARCASS TO MY LITTLE PEOPLE TO EAT!!!

HA-HA-HA-HA! YES! THAT'S THE LOOK!!
DESPAIR! MISERY! THAT'S MORE LIKE IT!!!
URRH
POOR, PITIFUL STEVE ...
AS A CHILD, HE WAS CRUSHED WHEN HE THOUGHT I BETRAYED HIM...
GOHO (COFF)
GOHO
F-FA-THER ...
...AND NOW HE'S BEEN OPENLY MOCKED AND DISOWNED BY HIS FATHER...
IN THE END, IT SEEMS I WILL HAVE NO CHOICE...
...BUT TO BECOME THE LORD OF THE SHADOWS... AND DESTROY THE WORLD...
WHY...DID IT ALL...HAVE TO TURN OUT...THIS WAY...?
WE'VE... BOTH ...
... BEEN VIC-TIMS ...
...PAWNS OF DES TINY...

HEH HEH ...

HA HA HA!

WHY DID IT TURN OUT THIS WAY? WHY THE LATE REGRETS ?

LOOK BACK ON WHAT YOU'VE DONE.

DEATH IS THE LEAST YOU DE-SERVE!

D... DAR-REN ...

YOU WERE RIGHT, STEVE...I DID PLOT WITH MR. CREPSLEY TO TAKE YOUR PLACE AS HIS ASSISTANT...
WE MADE A FOOL OF YOU, AND I'M GLAD.
THAT'S MY BOY!
ONE LAST DIG AT A DYING MAN!!
IF MR. CREPS-LEY WERE ALIVE...
...HE'D BE LAUGH-ING AT YOU NOW...
...JUST LIKE THE REST OF US ARE!!!
GYU (SQUEEZE)

DOSU
(THUK)
GASU
(THUK)
NOOOOOOO!!
NO, FATHER! YOU CANNOT INTERFERE IN THIS!
GET OUT OF MY WAY! THE FOOL'S GOING TO LET LEONARD KILL HIM!!!
WE HAVE TO STOP IT!!!

グイ..
GUI (GRAB)
TOO... LATE...
DES-TINY... REJECT-ED...
IF THE ONE WHO SURVIVES MUST BE THE LORD OF THE SHADOWS... THEN WHAT IF WE BOTH DIE?
I WILL DECIDE... MY OWN FUTURE...
YOUR DESTINY... COMES TO AN END HERE...

FORGIVE ME FOR WHAT I SAID TO YOU, STEVE...
JUST WHEN YOU HAD FINALLY REGAINED YOUR HUMAN-ITY...
...I HAD TO PUSH YOU AWAY FROM IT.
YOU FOOL... YOU HAD FINALLY WON...
YOU'LL... NEVER... CHANGE ...
BUT I GUESS... YOU'RE HAPPY THAT WAY...
... DAR-REN.
ZAPAA (SPLAASH)

LOOKING INTO HIS EYES NOW...
...IT'S ALL THERE. EVERYTHING WE HAD...
WE WERE AN UNSTOPPABLE DUO AT SOCCER...
...WEREN'T WE, STEVE?
IF ONLY I'D TAKEN A DIFFERENT PATH HERE OR THERE...
...THINGS WOULDN'T HAVE TURNED OUT THIS WAY...
IF ONLY WE COULD CHANGE THE PAST AND DO LIFE OVER...
WE MIGHT...
...HAVE BEEN ABLE...
...TO STAY... FRIENDS...

PISHI (CRAK)
DARREN IS GONE ...
YOU HAVE TO ACCEPT IT, FA-THER!
WE HAVE TO PULL HIM OUT! DARREN, DARREN!!
MY HOPES AND DREAMS !!!
FROM BEGINNING TO END, DARREN FOUGHT AGAINST THE DESTINY OF THE LORD OF THE SHADOWS.
AND NOW...
...WITH HIS OWN DEATH...
...HE HAS TRIUMPHED OVER FATE.

CHAPTER 111:
THE WORLD OF DRAGONS

I'M DEAD...

AND IN THE MINUTES, HOURS, DAYS SINCE MY DEATH—I CAN'T BEGIN TO GUESS HOW LONG IT'S BEEN—I HAVE BEEN FLOATING...

OR PERHAPS I'M SINKING... I HAVE NO WAY OF KNOWING...

WHERE AM I...?

THERE IS NO SENSATION, NO DEVELOPMENT... THE ONLY THING THAT EXISTS IS THE PAST...

AROUND... AND AROUND... AND AROUND...

THERE'S NO SENSE OF TIME PASSING SINCE MY BATTLE WITH STEVE.
HAVE I BEEN HERE A WEEK, A YEAR, A CENTURY? CAN'T TELL...
DOES THE WAR OF THE SCARS STILL RAGE...?
WITH THE DEATHS OF ME AND STEVE, HAS THE FIGHTING FINALLY COME TO AN END?
MEMORIES GNAW AWAY AT ME RELENT-LESSLY.
BUT I DIDN'T HAVE A CHOICE, TIME AND TIME AGAIN...
I COULD ONLY TAKE THE PLAN OF ACTION THAT SEEMED BEST AT THE TIME...
I'M TIRED OF THE PAIN OF THESE MEMORIES AND MISTAKES...
I TRY TO REMEMBER THE YOUNG DARREN SHAN...
HUMAN, HAPPY, NORMAL, INNOCENT...
RELIVING THE SIMPLE, CARE-FREE TIMES...

ARE YOU FLOATING THROUGH THIS SAME NOTHINGNESS, STEVE?
ARE YOU LOOKING BACK ON YOUR PAST OF MR. TINY'S MANIPULATION...
...AND SHEDDING TEARS OF REGRET AND REMORSE?
STEVE...
STEVE...
...STEVE...
WHAT ABOUT THE CIRQUE DU FREAK?
OR DEBBIE?
ARE THEY GRIEVING OVER MY DEATH AT THIS VERY MOMENT...?
IS HARKAT STILL ALIVE...?
WHAT ABOUT VANCHA, ALICE, THE VAMPIRITES? ARE THEY ALL SAFE AND SOUND?
BUT I'M ALWAYS BROUGHT BACK TO THE PAIN...
...AND NOTHING HAS CHANGED BUT THE PASSAGE OF TIME... AROUND AND AROUND...

TIME INCALCULABLE... DECADES, CENTURIES...
SO MANY FRIENDS LOST, SO MANY ENEMIES KILLED...
WAS THIS WAR TRULY UNAVOID-ABLE?
AND MORE TIME PASSES...
ALL THAT FLOATS OUT OF THE DARKNESS IS THE REGRET OF THE PAST...
THAT WAS...
KURDA...
THAT'S RIGHT, KURDA...
WHEN I FIRST BECAME A PRINCE, I DREAMED OF BEING A PEACEMAKER, TAKING UP WHERE KURDA LEFT OFF...
SOME-TIME IN THE FOL-LOWING YEARS...
...LIVING AS A VAMPIRE RUBBED OFF ON ME.

IT WAS THE FIRST—AND LAST—CHANCE FOR VAMPIRES AND VAMPANEZE...
...TO SIT DOWN AND TALK, TO AVOID CONFLICT...
...OUR FIRST CHANCE TO AVOID DISASTER...
I WENT ALONG WITH THE GENERAL OPINION, CLAMORING FOR BATTLE.
I EMBRACED THE WAR...
BUT WHY DIDN'T I DO IT SOONER...
...BEFORE SO MANY PEOPLE WERE KILLED?
IT DOESN'T MATTER THAT I'M THE SON OF DESMOND TINY...
I HAD THE POWER TO BREAK AWAY FROM THE DARK DESIGNS OF MY FATHER, WHICH I PROVED BY LETTING MYSELF DIE.
I WAS TOO LATE, TOO SLOW TO ACT AT ALL TIMES...
I NEVER FOUND MY OWN VOICE AND WILL, IN ANYTHING.
I WAS MERELY BUFFETED BY EVENTS BEYOND MY CONTROL...
WHY...?
WHY... WHY...

MADNESS WOULD ALMOST BE AN IMPROVEMENT UPON THIS...
THERE IS NO OTHER ESCAPE... FROM THE RELENTLESS CYCLE OF REGRET AND PAIN...
GABOO (BLOOSH)
IF ONLY...
...I COULD FORGET... IT ALL... BUT THE FLOW... OF TIME...
... IS SO... SUFFOCATING ...
ENDLESS... END... LESS...
......
...
PAIN!! WEIGHT!!!
RISING... SOMEONE PULLING
BUCHI (RIP)

KUR...
DA...
(SPLASH)

OH, THANK GOODNESS!
I DIDN'T THINK WE WOULD BE ABLE TO PULL YOU UP!
...
WHUH...
...E... EVAN... NA...?
EASY, DON'T TRY TO SPEAK. IT WILL TAKE A FEW HOURS...
... FOR THE EFFECTS OF THE LAKE TO WEAR OFF.
SENSATIONS... RETURNING...
I FEEL EARTH... WIND...
SUN ...
ARE THOSE... DRAG-ONS?
I SEE... I'VE BEEN PULLED OUT OF THE LAKE OF SOULS AND BROUGHT BACK TO LIFE...
WHICH MEANS I'M IN THE...

QUITE THE ONE FOR SURPRISES, ISN'T HE—OUR FATHER?
HE TRAPPED YOUR SOUL IN THE LAKE BEFORE IT COULD TRAVEL ONWARD TO PARADISE...FOR THOUSANDS OF YEARS...
THOU... SANDS?
SFX: BURU (SHIVER) BURU
YES. THIS IS FAR, FAR AFTER THE TIME THAT YOU AND HARKAT CAME HERE.
I... SEE...
SO THAT'S... WHY KURDA...
KUR-DA?
AHH, I SEE...
LOOK AT ALL OF THE DRAGONS ...
IT IS TRULY THEIR AGE NOW.
PICK ONE OUT OF THE CROWD.
CALL IT DOWN HERE.
HUH ...?

CALL THEM, THE WA YOU USED TO CALL MADAM OCTA.
YOU CAN CONTROL DRAGONS AS YOU CON-TROLLED YOUR PET SPIDER.
....
BUWA (WHOOSH)
WELL DONE... YOU ARE IN CON-TROL.
YOU TRULY ARE DES-MOND TINY'S SON.
STOP! LEAVE HIM ALONE!!!
IT'S IN-CREDIBLE. THIS IS THE FIRST TIME I HAVE SEEN ONE UP SO CLOSE.
OUR FATHER OUTDID HIMSELF WITH THIS CREATION.
MR. TINY MADE THE DRAGONS ?

WITH OUR FATHER'S HELP, YOUR FRIEND ALAN MORRIS MADE A BREAK-THROUGH THAT ALLOWED THEM TO BE CLONED FROM A COMBINATION OF DINOSAUR CELLS.
THE DRAGONS WERE AN IM-PORTANT PIECE OF FATHER'S PLAN.
ALAN? YOU'RE TELLING ME THAT ALAN MOR-RIS MADE DRAGONS !?
HE'S A GENETICIST— QUITE A FAMOUS ONE!
BIG INTO CLONING.
REALLY? ALAN?
YEAH! I TOLD HIM...
AS LONG AS YOU DON'T CLONE YOURSELF! ONE ALAN IS ENOUGH!
BUT THERE IS MORE TO THIS STORY THAN THAT...
DO YOU RECOGNIZE THIS?
PAA (GLOW)
OF COURSE, THE ONE YOU SAW WAS LIKELY MUCH LARGER...
IT'S...THE STONE OF BLOOD!!!
THAT'S RIGHT. A DRAGON'S BRAIN.
OUR FATHER TOOK THE BRAIN OF A DRAGON INTO THE PAST AND GAVE IT TO THE VAMPIRES.
A PAR-TICULARLY LARGE EXAMPLE OF A DRAGON, OF COURSE.
IF THE VAMPIRES WIN THE WAR OF THE SCARS, THEY WILL USE THE STONE TO CONTROL THE DRAGONS AND THE SKIES.
THE AMPANEZE OULD NOT SE IT, AND HUS IF THEY N THE WAR, HEY WOULD BE PITTED GAINST THE DRAGONS.

ABOVE ALL ELSE, OUR FATHE CRAVE CHAOS
STABIL-ITY BORES HIM. HE HAS NO INTEREST IN SEEING ANY RACE RULE FOR-EVER.
THE EGYPTIANS, THE PERSIANS, THE BRITISH...
WHAT DESMOND HELPS CREATE, HE LATER DESTROYS.
IN ORDER TO BRING DOWN A HUMAN EMPIRE, A NEWER, STRONGER EMPIRE MUST BE INTRODUCED.
OUR FATHER HAS HAD HIS HAND IN MOST OF MANKIND'S MOST NOTABLE BREAK-THROUGHS.
ARCHITEC-TURAL, TECHNICAL, MEDICAL.
THE ONLY AREA WHERE HE HAD NO REAL POWER...
...WAS THAT OF LITERA-TURE.
DESMON IS NOT A FICTIONA DREAME REALITY IS EVERY THING T HIM.
HE HAS NO INTEREST IN THE WONDERFUL STORIES OF MANKIND.
WRITERS HAVE ALWAYS BEEN ALIEN TO HIM—HE DOES NOT READ OR TAKE NOTICE OF WORKS OF FICTION.

IN THE MIDDLE OF THE TWENTIETH CENTURY, OUR FATHER DECIDED MAN-KIND WAS TAKING A PATH TOWARD PEACE.
AND IN THE END, HE SETTLED ON VAMPIRES AND VAMPANEZE TO TAKE OVER THE REINS.
IT'S TIME TO ASK WHAT I'VE BEEN AFRAID TO HEAR ...
WHAT HAPPENED TO THE WAR OF THE SCARS? DID I DIE IN VAIN?
BASA (FLAP)
BASA
IT'S LATE. TIME FOR US TO MOVE ON.
THE NIGHTS ARE COLDER IN THIS TIME.
SFX: BUTSU (MUTTER) BUTSU
GOGO
GOGOGO (RUMBLE)
WAIT A MINUTE... WE AREN'T GOING TO PULL STEVE OUT?
HE'S DOWN THERE, ISN'T HE?

WE CAN DO NOTHING FOR STEVE.
HE IS LOST TO THE LAKE FOREVER.
KOHH... (WSHH)

I ASKED MY FATHER TO RELEASE YOU AND STEVE FROM THE LAKE OF SOULS.
WE AGREED A DEAL AFTER MUCH DEBATE, BUT HE WOULD NOT ALLOW ME TO SAVE THE BOTH OF YOU.
WHAT SORT OF DEAL?
I AGREED TO BEAR A VAMPIRE OR VAMPANEZE CHILD...
...AND HE AGREED TO RELEASE ONE OF THE TWO OF YOU.

OOO (WHOOSH)
A CHILD? I KNEW YOU COULD GIVE BIRTH TO VAMPIRE BABIES...
...BUT NOT VAMPANEZE AS WELL...
BUT I THOUGHT VAMPIRES COULDN'T BEAR CHILDREN THE NORMAL WAY...
SHE IS THE ONLY WOMAN IN THE ENTIRE WORLD WHO CAN GIVE BIRTH TO VAMPIRE CHILDREN.
WH-WHAT DOES THIS MEAN...?
I CAN HAVE CHILDREN WITH EITHER OF THE FAMILY OF NIGHT-WALKERS.
AND AS THEY WILL HAVE SOME OF MY POWERS AND CAN LIVE BY DAY, THEY WILL BE A NEW BREED, AN ADVANCED RACE.
MR TINY BELIEVES HAT THOSE CHILDREN WILL DRIVE THE CLANS APART.
WHAT!?
TWO YEARS AFTER YOUR DEATH, MY FATHER SENT ME FORWARD IN TIME TO THIS MOMENT IN THE FUTURE.
IN THE "PRESENT," THE WAR OF THE SCARS STILL RAGES.
BUT PERSUASIVE LEADERS ARE PUSHING FOR PEACE.
VANCHA AND HARKAT MULDS ON THE SIDE OF THE VAMPIRES, GANNEN HARST FOR THE VAMPANEZE.
DEBBIE AND ALICE ARE INVOLVED AS WELL.
A CHILD OF MINE COULD CHANGE ALL OF THAT AND DIVIDE THE CLANS AGAIN.
BUT THAT WOULD LEAD TO MORE FIGHTING AT THE TIME WHEN PEACE IS CLOSEST!!

OF COURSE. THAT IS OUR FATHER'S INTENT.
PEACE IS THE LAST THING HE WANTS TO SEE.
YOU AGREED TO THAT? YOU SOLD OUT THE WORLD JUST TO HELP ME!?
SO WHOSE CHILD IS IT?
HEH...
VAMPIRE OR VAMPANEZE!?
BOTH...AND NEITHER...
...
WHAT DO YOU MEAN?
I AM HAVING TWINS.
EACH CHILD CARRIES BOTH VAMPIRE AND VAMPANEZE BLOOD...
...AND ONE-THIRD OF MY OWN.
ONE BY VANCHA, ONE BY GANNEN...
THAT'S HOW I'VE TRICKED HIM: MY CHILDREN ARE AN ENTIRELY NEW RACE.
RATHER THAN DIVIDING, THEY WILL BRING THE CLANS CLOSER TOGETHER.

WHAT'S MORE, HE HAS NO IDEA OF THE TRUTH.
WE'RE GOING TO CREATE PEACE, DARREN, IN SPITE OF OUR FATHER.
THAT'S WHAT YOU TAUGHT ME—WE DON'T HAVE TO ACCEPT DESTINY, OR DES TINY.
BUT THE PLAN ISN'T FLAW-LESS.
IF WE ARE TO CHANGE OUR FATHER'S IDEAL WORLD OF CHAOS INTO ONE OF PEACE AND BEAUTY...
...THERE IS MUCH LEFT TO BE DONE...
BUT THIS IS SOME-THING BEYOND STEVE'S REACH.
ONLY YOU CAN HELP US, DARREN.
THAT IS WHY I ASKED DESMOND TO FREE YOUR SPIRIT, RATHER THAN HIS.
IT IS TIME FOR THE FINAL PUSH, DARREN.
THOUGH YOUR HEART MAY BE HEAVY, YOU MUST CONFRONT HIM.

THIS IS OUR FATHER'S STRONG-HOLD.
CON-FRONT ...
...MR. TINY...

CHAPTER 112: GREEN BLOOD

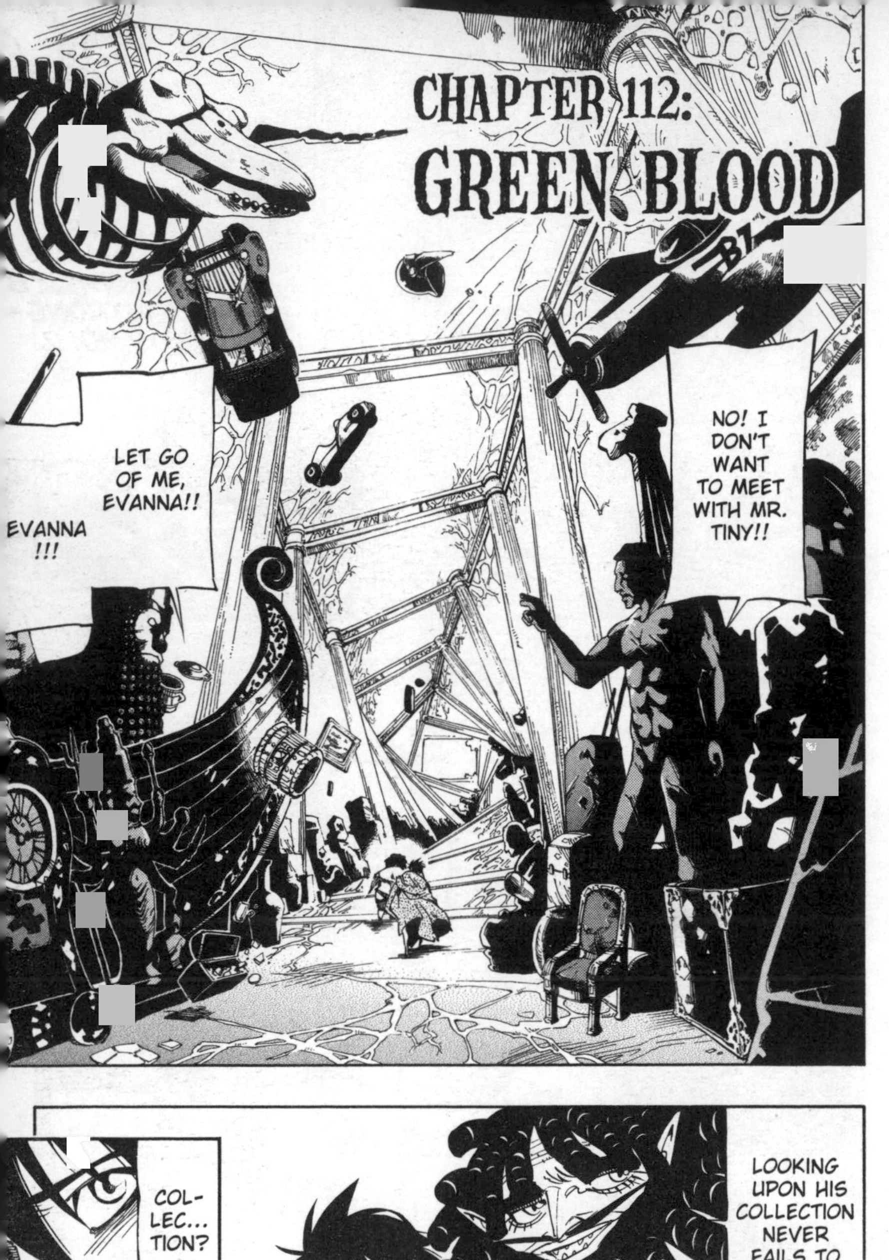

NO! I DON'T WANT TO MEET WITH MR. TINY!!
LET GO OF ME, EVANNA!!
EVANNA!!!

LOOKING UPON HIS COLLECTION NEVER FAILS TO INSPIRE A SIGH OR TWO...
COL-LEC... TION?

WAIT A SECOND ...
THESE ALL LOOK... FAMILIAR ...
THERE'S THE THINKER, AND VAN GOGH'S CYPRESS, AND...
YES, THE MONA LISA. ALL ORIGINAL.
ORIGINAL? IT MUST BE A REPLICA. THE ORIGINAL'S IN THE LOUVRE...
THE ONE IN THE LOUVRE IS THE COPY, DARREN.
SOME OF OUR FATHER'S LITTLE PEOPLE ARE CREATED FROM THE SOULS OF ART-ISTS. THEY MAKE PERFECT COPIES, SO IDENTICAL EVEN THE ACTUAL ARTIST CANNOT TELL THE DIFFERENCE.
OUR FATHER IS A SELFISH MAN. HE ALWAYS KEEPS THE BEST FOR HIM-SELF.
WHAT HE WANTS, HE TAKES—AND HE NORMALLY WANTS THE BEST OF EVERYTHING.
THE ONLY EXCEPTION IS BOOKS.
HE NEVER READS WORKS OF FICTION. HE COULDN'T EVEN NAME AN AUTHOR...
YOU SAID THAT ALREADY. I DON'T CARE ABOUT WHAT HE LIKES OR DISLIKES!

LOOK! I'M NOT GOING TO SEE MR. TINY, AND THAT'S THAT!!
STOP !!
YOU'VE BEEN BROUGHT BACK TO LIFE NOW THAT YOU'VE BEEN PULLED OUT OF THE LAKE OF SOULS.
BUT YOUR SOUL IS STILL TRAPPED WITHIN THE LAKE.
IF NOTHING IS CHANGED, YOU WILL LIVE OUT THE REST OF YOUR LIFE AND THEN RETURN TO THE LAKE OF SOULS WHEN YOU DIE.
IF YOUR SOUL IS TO BE EPARATED FROM THE AKE AND SENT TO PARADISE NSTEAD...
...YOU MUST SEE OUR FATHER AND HAVE HIM TURN YOU INTO A LITTLE PERSON.
WHAT... DID YOU SAY? TURN ME...INTO A LITTLE PERSON?
ASK NO MORE QUES- TIONS. DESMOND WILL EXPLAIN THE REST TO YOU.
BUT —!
WELL, WELL ...
IF IT ISN'T THE YOUNG MARTYR HIMSELF.
BURU (SHIVER)

MEET ANYONE INTERESTING IN THE LAKE OF SOULS?
IF I'D KNOWN WHAT A NUISANCE YOU WERE GOING TO BE ...
...I'D NEVER HAVE SPAWNED YOU.
TOO LATE NOW.
IGNORE HIM, DAR-REN...

NO, IT ISN'T. I COULD GO BACK AND ERASE YOU FROM THE PAST!
YOUR SOUL WOULDN'T JUST BE DESTROYED— IT WOULD BE UNMADE COMPLETELY!!
THE UNIVERSE WOULD REPLACE YOU. SOMEBODY ELSE WOULD BECOME THE YOUNGEST-EVER VAMPIRE PRINCE, HUNT FOR THE VAMPANEZE LORD, ET CETERA!
SOME-BODY... ELSE? WHO WOULD THAT BE?
YOU LIKELY CANNOT GRASP SUCH A CONCEPT, BUT THE UNIVERSE KEEPS A NATURAL ORDER.
THERE IS A HIGHER POWER THAT KEEPS IT ALL IN LINE.
NOW THAT IT HAS HAPPENED, THE WAR OF THE SCARS BETWEEN THE VAMPIRES AND VAMPANEZE CAN NEVER BE CHANGED...
...BUT THE INDIVIDUAL PLAYERS CAN BE REPLACED!!
IT IS TRUE, DARREN. FOR INSTANCE, YOU COULD NOT TRAVEL TO THE PAST AND PREVENT WWII...
EVEN IF YOU KILLED ADOLF HITLER, THE UNIVERSE WOULD CRE-ATE SOME-ONE TO FILL HIS SHOES.
......
FATHER, YOU KNOW YOU AREN'T GOING TO GET RID OF DARREN.
BUT I COULD!
YES, BUT YOU WON'T. WE HAVE AN AGREEMENT. I'VE UPHELD MY END.
NOW IT'S YOUR TURN.

EVANNA'S TOLD YOU THE PLAN HASN'T SHE?
IT'S TIME TO RECAST YOU.
TAKE OFF THE BLANKET AND HOP INTO THE POOL.
GOPO (BLUP)
GOPO
THAT WILL TURN ME INTO A LITTLE PERSON?
CORRECT.
HOW DOES IT WORK?
THIS GREEN LIQUID IS THE SOUP OF CREATION.
IT WILL BECOME YOUR BLOOD, THE FUEL ON WHICH YOUR NEW BODY RUNS.
YOUR FLESH, BRAIN, ORGANS AND SOUL WILL DISSOLVE WHEN YOU STEP IN.
I SHALL MIX IT ALL UP AND BUILD A NEW BODY OUT OF THE MESS.
THOSE WHO'VE BEEN THROUGH IT TELL ME IT'S A MOST TERRIBLY PAINFUL PROCEDURE...
...THE WORST THEY'VE EVER KNOWN...
HEE-HEE-HEE...
WHAT MAKES YOU THINK I'M GOING TO DO IT?
YOU DON'T HAVE TO...
IF YOU RESIST THE CHOICE, YOU DON'T GO IN.
AND NO DEAL WITH MY DAUGHTER IF YOU DON'T.

IT DOESN'T MAKE SENSE...
HOW CAN I HELP BRING ABOUT PEACE BETWEEN THE VAMPIRES AND VAMPANEZE BY GOING THROUGH A LOAD OF PAIN AND BECOMING A LITTLE PERSON?
I DON'T SEE WHY THIS IS NECES-SARY.
IT IS ENTIRELY FOR YOUR SAKE.
THIS IS FOR YOU, DARREN.
IT HAS NOTHING TO DO WITH WHAT IS HAPPENING IN THE PRESENT, OR THE WAR OF THE SCARS.
THAT'S RIGHT.
AND I JUST JUMP INTO THE POOL?
IF I BECOME A LITTLE PERSON, WILL YOU REMOVE MY MEMORY AND MAKE ME YOUR SERVANT, LIKE HARKAT?

I ADMIT I QUITE LIKE THE IDEA OF HAVING YOU TOADY FOR ME FOR A FEW MILLION YEARS OR SO...
...BUT MY DAUGHTER WAS VERY PRECISE WHEN IT CAME TO THE TERMS OF OUR AGREEMENT.
YOU WON'T BE ABLE TO TALK, BUT THAT'S THE ONLY RESTRICTION.
AND IT'S BECAUSE I'M SICK OF LISTENING TO YOU!!!
TRUST ME, DARREN. PLEASE...
THERE IS MUCH LEFT TO BE DONE... ONLY YOU CAN HELP US, DARREN.
OKAY ...
I TRUST YOU.
BA (LEAP)

AGONY !!
...URN-
...ING !!!
!!
!!!
FLESH STRIPPED FROM MY BODY...
BONES EXPOSED ...
MELTING TO THE MARROW ...
SHEER TOR-TURE ...
DOBOH (KABLOOSH)
...
FU (SWISH)
THERE GOES...SAM GREST'S SOUL...
SAM...
THANK YOU...
...AND GOOD-BYE...

ALL DIS-SOLVED ...
LET US BEGIN.
I AM THE LIQUID...AND THE LIQUID IS ME...
IT'S A STRANGE FEELING...
OUT OF THE LIQUID...MY NEW BONES...FLESH... ORGANS...
CONDENSED, COMPRESSED... SUCKED INTO VEINS...
TOKUN (BADUM)
TOKUN
I CAN HEAR... MY NEW... PULSE...
SET TO FLOW... THROUGH MY ENTIRE FORM...
WHEW ...

ANOTHER PERFECT CREATION, EVEN IF I DO SAY SO MYSELF.

GOSHI (RUB)

GOSHI

MY SENSES ... ARE COMING BACK ...

MY EYE-SIGHT IS HAZY... AND GREEN...

FLAW-LESS.

...

YORO

YORO (WOBBLE)

ZUDA (SLIP)

WALK AROUND. IT WON'T TAKE YOU LONG TO GET USED TO YOUR NEW SHAPE.

YOUR CREATOR NEEDS A REST.

EASY, DAR-REN ...

MY BODY FEELS HEAVY... AND CLUMSY ...

AND I CAN'T... SPEAK...

I DON'T HAVE A TONGUE... OR TEETH !!

YOU WON'T BE ALIVE LONG ENOUGH TO EAT.

YOU PROBABLY WON'T NEED A MASK, BUT BETTER SAFE THAN SORRY...

LET ME HELP YOU PUT THIS ROBE ON.
WON'T BE ALIVE LONG!? WHAT DOES THAT MEAN!? HAVE YOU DECEIVED ME AS WELL, EVANNA?
THEY'RE SEWED INTO THE ROBE.
PON (PAT)
SO DESMOND DOESN'T FIND OUT...
REMEMBER WHY WE BROUGHT YOU BACK, DARREN.
DON'T EVER FORGET.
IF WE ARE TO FREE YOUR SOUL AND DEFY OUR FATHER'S WILL...YOU MUST COMPLETE THE ROLE THAT IS LEFT TO YOU.
IF THIS ALL WORKS, YOU AND STEVE WILL BE FREED FROM THE CYCLE OF DESTINY...
THE REST DEPENDS ON YOU.
THIS IS GOOD-BYE, DARREN...
HE'S READY, FATHER.
GOOD.
OOOO (WHOOSH)

DON'T GET ANY SMART IDEAS BACK THERE.
I DON'T KNOW WHAT YOU AND SHE THINK YOU'RE GETTING UP TO...
...BUT YOU CAN'T CHANGE THE PAST, SO DON'T BOTHER TRYING.
NOW GO.
EVA ...
MY POOR FAILURE OF A SON...
SU (SWISH)
DO (THOOM)

......
......
IS THIS ...?
......
SUSKIN (TEXTILES) LT

CIRQUE DU...
......
CIRQUE FREAK
THESE FLYERS ...
HEY! YOU THERE!
ZUSHA (STOMP)
ZA (ZSHH)
ARE YOU THE ONE PASTING UP THESE FLYERS FOR THE FREAK SHOW ALL OVER TOWN?
HAVE I...
...SEEN HIM BE-FORE?
HAND THOSE OVER !!
WE'RE SEIZING THESE!
W-WAIT! IT'S NOT ME!

I CAN'T SPEAK!
LET GO!!
BUN (YANK)
AAAAH!
DOGA (THWUD)
UGH
!!!
OH, NO! I DIDN'T MEAN TO...
AND NOW YOU ATTACK OFFICERS OF THE LAW!?
!!
GUA (SWOOP)

DA (DASH)
DOSHA (THWOMP)
I REMEMBER THIS! I SAW THIS YEARS AGO!
THAT WAS MR. DALTON, THE TEACHER!!
GOING THROUGH THAT RED GATE SENT ME BACK IN TIME TO MY CHILDHOOD!!
LET'S GO, STEVE!
WE'VE GOT TO FOL-LOW HIM!
WAIT, DARREN!
THIS IS CRAZY!

IT'S THAT FATEFUL NIGHT, EIGHTEEN YEARS AGO!!!
!?

CHAPTER 113:
THAT FATEFUL DAY
LADIES AND GENTLE-MEN...
...WELCOME TO THE CIRQUE DU FREAK...
...HOME OF THE WORLD'S MOST REMARK-ABLE HUMAN BEINGS!!
IS THE WOLF-MAN ALL READY?
YES.
THE WORLD'S MOST TERRIFYING SHOW WILL SOON BEGIN.
YOU WILL FORGIVE ME FOR INTRODUC-ING OUR FIRST ACT IN HUSHED TONES.
THE WOLF-MAN...

GRAWR!
AWOOO!
AM I... ...DREAMING ALL OF THIS?
I'M BACK. IT'S EIGHTEEN YEARS AGO, ON THE VERY NIGHT...
...THAT STEVE AND I FIRST VISITED THE CIRQUE DU FREAK!!
HEY, YOU DROPPED THIS.
SHAN-CUS? NO...
EVRA!!

YOU'RE ALMOST UP. ONE, TWO...
C'MON! KEEP IT TOGETHER!
AAAAAHH!!
GO!!
BUT... THAT'S NOT MINE...
ZAWA
ZAWA (MURMUR)
POWDER AND NEEDLE.
THE ARM AS WELL, IF YOU PLEASE.
THAT'S RIGHT. THE WOLF-MAN CHEWED OFF THE LADY'S ARM WHEN SHE STUMBLED AND FELL IN THE AISLE...

PARA (SPRINKLE)
PARA
BUTSU (SHHP)
OHH!
IT MOVES! I CAN FEEL MY HAND AGAIN!
PACHI (CLAP)
PACHI
PACHI

I'M UP NEXT!
I REMEMBER MY SHOCK WHEN HANS TOLD ME...
EVERY ASPECT OF THE WOLF-MAN'S RAMPAGE IS PLANNED OUT.
EVERY-THING ASIDE FROM THE ARM ALL RIGHT? THANKS, AS AL-WAYS.
OH, I'M FINE. I TRUST YOU AND MR. TALL.
AHH, I FEEL DIZZY ...
I CAN SEE ME AND STEVE AS KIDS IN THE AUDIENCE... BACK WHEN WE WERE BEST FRIENDS.
HOW MANY TIMES HAVE I WISHED I COULD RETURN TO THIS DAY AND CHANGE EVERY-THING?
THANK YOU FOR THAT RIVETING PERFOR-MANCE, HANS.
NEXT IN OUR SHOCK-ING SHOW ...
ZA (ZSHH)
I KNOW EXACTLY WHAT HAPPENS AFTER THIS...
BUT WHAT CAN I DO ABOUT IT?
I'M STUCK IN THE BODY OF A MUTE LITTLE PERSON ...

HMPH!
BASA (FLAP)
......
......!!
AND NOW, MR. CREPS-LEY...
...AND HIS PER-FORMING SPIDER, MADAM OCTA!!!

HIS TRADE-MARK SCAR ON THE LEFT CHEEK.
THAT CROP OF ORANGE HAIR.
MR. CREPSLEY !!
I NEVER THOUGHT I'D SEE HIM AGAIN ...
PACHI (CLAP)
PACHI
PACHI
PACHI
I WANT TO RUN UP AND HUG HIM.
I'VE BEEN DYING TO SEE HIM AGAIN ...
I WANT TO TELL HIM HOW IMPORTANT HE WAS TO ME...
MR. CREPS-LEY!!!
I LOVE YOU...
YOU WERE A FATHER TO ME...

AND EVEN IF I WROTE SOME-THING, MR. CREPSLEY IS ILLITER-ATE.
IT'S NO USE... I CAN'T SPEAK.
BUT MOST OF ALL ...
...MR. CREPSLEY DOESN'T KNOW WHO I AM AT THIS POINT. I CAN'T RELY ON HIM...
WAA (RAHHH)
PACHI
PACHI
PACHI
PACHI
THAT WAS INCREDIBLE! AMAZING! DID YOU SEE THAT, STEVE? DID YOU!?
YEAH, I SURE DID.

AND NOW THAT STEVE REALIZES MR. CREPSLEY IS A VAMPIRE ...
LET'S SEE... THIS IS ABOUT THE RIGHT MOMENT ...
TAKE CARE ON YOUR WAY HOME!
GAYA (MURMUR)
GET YOUR SOUVENIRS IN THE GIFT SHOP !!
GACHA (CLICK)
I JUST HAVE TO WAIT IN THIS SPOT...
MR. TINY SAID THAT I COULDN'T CHANGE WHAT HAPPENED.
BUT I CAN CHANGE THE PLAYERS INVOLVED ...
AAH!

IF I'M TO FREE YOUR SOUL...
...THERE'S SOMETHING LEFT TO BE DONE.
AND IT'S ALL UP TO ME...
DON (THUD)
HEY, OPEN UP!
OPEN THE DOOR !!
DON
THAT'S WHAT EVANNA SAID.
WHY WAS I BROUGHT BACK TO LIFE?
HAA (HUFF)
HAA
STUPID THING WON'T OPEN.
WHY WAS I GIVEN THIS LIMITED BODY...
...AND SENT BACK TO THIS DAY?
GOKU (GULP)
WELL, I'M NOT AFRAID ...
NEVER FEAR, HOTSHOT SHAN IS HERE!!!
I DON'T KNOW IF I'M MAKING THE RIGHT CHOICE...
...BUT IT'S WHAT I CAN DO, AND THAT'S THAT.

BA
(LEAP)
!?
GUI
(YANK)
DA
(STOMP)
DA
DA
BAN
(TOSS)

DON (WHAM)
WAIT! STEVE'S IN THERE!
MY FRIEND'S INSIDE!!
DON
MERI (SCRATCH)
MERI
MEGI (SCRITCH)
GII (CREAK)
!!!!!
AAAH!!!
THAT SHOULD KEEP YOUNG ME AND STEVE FROM BEING DRAGGED INTO THE WAR OF THE SCARS.

NOW I DON'T KNOW MR. CREPSLEY IS A VAMPIRE...
...OR THAT STEVE WANTS TO BE A VAMPIRE HIMSELF...
I WANT YOU TO MAKE ME A VAMPIRE!
I NEVER SAW WHAT HAPPENED BETWEEN THE TWO OF THEM FROM THE BALCONY OF THE THEATER.
AS IT HAPPENED BEFORE, MR. CREPSLEY WILL REJECT STEVE DUE TO HIS BLOOD.
I'M SURE HE'LL BE ENRAGED AT THIS...
...BUT HE'LL SOON GET OVER IT AND STOP OBSESSING OVER BEING A VAMPIRE.
SINCE I NEVER SAW THEIR CONFRONTATION, I'LL HAVE NO REASON TO FEAR STEVE...
...AND HE WILL HAVE NO REASON TO BE SUSPICIOUS OF ME.
I CAN'T BE SURE IF YOUNGER ME WILL COME BACK TO STEAL MADAM OCTA OR NOT...
...BUT WITH THE SCARE I JUST GAVE HIM, I THINK SHE'LL BE SAFE...

THE WAR OF THE SCARS WILL HAPPEN, ONE WAY OR AN-OTHER.
BUT NOW THAT STEVE AND I WILL NO LONGER BE VAMPANEZE AND VAMPIRE ...
...IT WON'T BE US PARTICIPATING IN THE WAR, IF EVANNA AND DESMOND TINY ARE TO BE BELIEVED.
I FEEL BAD FOR WHATEVER UNFORTUNATE BOY ENDS UP LIVING THE TERRIBLE LIFE I LED.
......
NO, WAIT.
BOY? WHO'S TO SAY IT WON'T BE A GIRL?
THE PRO-TAGONIST OF FATE'S SCENARIO WILL CHANGE, WHICH MEANS OTHER FACTS COULD CHANGE AS WELL.
IF IT IS A GIRL WHO TAKES MY PLACE IN THE STORY ...
COULD THAT MEAN DEBBIE'S ROLE WILL BE PLAYED BY A BOY?
IT COULD BE SAM!
...I'LL BET MR. CREPSLEY HAS AN EVEN HARDER TIME THAN HE DID WITH ME ...

BUT THIS IS JUST IN MY IMAGINATION.

ALL I CAN SAY FOR CERTAIN IS THAT YOUNG "ME" WILL LEAD A NORMAL LIFE NOW.

ANOTHER VERSION OF ME WILL TASTE THE LIFE I NEVER HAD...

LIFE AS A HUMAN BEING.

IF IT WERE SIMPLY A MATTER OF SETTING MY SOUL FREE, THEY COULD HAVE JUST PULLED ME OUT OF THE LAKE OF SOULS AND MADE ME A LITTLE PERSON...

IF WE ARE TO FREE YOUR SOUL...

...YOU MUST COMPLETE THE ROLE THAT IS LEFT TO YOU.

YOU MUST BE TURNED INTO A LITTLE PERSON.

...BUT EVANNA WENT ONE STEP FURTHER AND TRIED TO SAVE NOT JUST MY SOUL, BUT MY LIFE AS WELL...

I WISH I COULD SEE THIS TO THE END, BUT I THINK MY TIME'S NEARLY UP.

IT'S LIKE WHAT HAPPENED WITH HARKAT...

MY BODY'S BREAKING DOWN... IN MOMENTS, I'LL BE GONE.

I'VE DONE EVERYTHING I NEEDED TO...
GORO (ROLL)
NOW I JUST WAIT FOR THIS BODY TO TURN TO DUST...
GORI (POKE)
?
MOZO (RUSTLE)
MOZO
BUT ... THESE ARE...
...MY...
... DIARIES ?
Darren Shan
SHAN
WHY DID YOU GIVE ME THESE, EVANNA?
LET ME HELP YOU PUT THIS ROBE ON.
THEY'RE SEWED INTO THE ROBE.
SO DESMOND DOESN'T FIND OUT...

"OUR FATHER HATES BOOKS."
"THIS IS SOMETHING BEYOND STEVE'S REACH."
"ONLY YOU CAN HELP US, DARREN."
NI (GRIN)
HA-HA... GOOD OLD EVANNA.
YORO (WOBBLE)
TRUE, ONLY I CAN DO THIS.
I MIGHT BE ABLE TO PREVENT MR. TINY'S SCHEMES WITH THESE DIARIES.
NOW I KNOW WHAT SHE WAS TALKING ABOUT!

CHAPTER 114: SKY

I'VE KEPT A DIARY FOR ABOUT AS LONG AS I CAN REMEMBER.

EVERYTHING IMPORTANT FROM MY LIFE HAS BEEN WRITTEN DOWN...

EVANNA BROUGHT THE DIARY UP TO DATE AFTER MY DEATH.
SHE DESCRIBED ALL THAT HAPPENED ON THAT BLOOD-DRENCHED NIGHT, AND EVEN BEYOND THAT...
SHE KEPT A DETAILED ACCOUNT OF MY RESCUE FROM THE LAKE OF SOULS...
...AND THEN MY RETURN, THE WAY I SCARED THE ORIGINAL DARREN AWAY, AND...
I DON'T KNOW WHAT SHE WROTE IN THE LAST FEW PAGES. I DIDN'T READ THAT FAR.
I DON'T WANT TO READ ABOUT MY FINAL ACTIONS AND THOUGHTS IN A BOOK.

I'D RATHER FIND OUT MYSELF.
KON
KON (KNOCK)

CHAPTER 114:
SKY

GACHA (CLICK)
WHAT DO YOU WANT?
NU (LOOM)
......
THEN WHAT ...?
IS THIS A MESSAGE FROM DES-MOND?
BUN (SHAKE)
BUN
!!?

BA (LIFT)
NO! IT CAN'T BE!!!
EVAN-NA...
IS THIS MY SISTER'S WORK? I NEVER THOUGHT SHE'D GET INVOLVED...
HA HA...
I IMAGINE THERE'S MORE TO I THAN JUS FREEING YOUR SOUL...
...BUT I WON'T PRESS YOU FOR INFORMATION— BETTER FOR ALL CONCERNED IF I DON'T KNOW.
BAN
BAN (WHAP)
Darren Shan
YOU WANT ME TO READ THEM?

CHI (TOK)
CHI (TIK)
SIGH...
I SEE...
Darren Shan
EVANNA NOT ONLY SAVED YOUR SOUL—SHE GAVE THE OLD YOU HIS NORMAL LIFE BACK.
YES! HE UNDERSTANDS!
YOUR PLAN IS CLEAR TO ME NOW. I WILL KEEP THESE SAFE UNTIL THE TIME IS RIGHT.
THEN I WILL SEND THEM TO...
...WHO? AN AUTHOR? A PUBLISHER?
OR THE PERSON YOU HAVE BECOME?

VERY WELL. I CANNOT SAY WHAT HE WILL DO WITH THESE...
...BUT I'LL DO AS YOU REQUEST.
I NOW KNOW WHY EVANNA COMMENTED ON MR. TINY NOT BEING A READER.
HE HAS NOTHING TO DO WITH BOOKS. HE DOESN'T PAY ATTENTION TO NOVELS OR OTHER WORKS OF FICTION.
IF, MANY YEARS FROM NOW, AN ADULT DARREN SHAN COMES ALONG AND PUBLISHES A SERIES OF BOOKS ABOUT VAMPIRES, MR. TINY WON'T KNOW ABOUT IT.
AS THE WAR OF THE SCARS COMES TO A WARY PAUSE AND LEADERS ON BOTH SIDES TRY TO FORGE A NEW ERA OF PEACE...
...MY DIARIES WILL HIT BOOK-STORES AROUND THE WORLD.
Darren Sha
HERE.
Children's Books
VAMPIRES AND VAMPANEZE WILL BE ABLE TO READ MY STORY!
THEY'LL DISCOVER MORE ABOUT MR. TINY THAN THEY EVER IMAGINED.

ARMED WITH THAT KNOWLEDGE, AND UNITED BY THE BIRTH OF EVANNA'S CHILDREN...
...I'M CERTAIN THEY'LL BAND TOGETHER AND DO ALL THEY CAN TO STOP HIM.
I CAN PRACTICALLY SEE MR. TINY NOW—FACE TWISTED WITH RAGE, TEETH GNASHING.
Darren Shan

IF THE ADULT ME READS THE DIARIES ALL THE WAY TO THE END AND BELIEVES THEY'RE REAL, HE'LL KNOW WHAT TO DO.
REWRITE THEM, FICTIONALIZE IT A BIT, CREATE AN ACTION-PACKED ADVENTURE. AND THEN, WHEN HE'S DONE ALL THAT—SELL IT!

ONCE IT'S A BIG HIT, HE COULD HAVE IT TURNED INTO A MOVIE—MAYBE EVEN A COMIC BOOK!
KATA (TAP)
KATA
AM I BEING REALISTIC?
MAYBE I'M JUST DREAMING. BUT IT COULD HAPPEN. I'M PROOF THAT STRANGER THINGS HAVE TAKEN PLACE.

I'VE ALWAYS been fascinated by spiders.
MR. TINY LOOKED DOWN UPON MERE "WORDS," BUT WORDS HAVE THE POWER TO ALTER THE FUTURE AND CHANGE THE WORLD.
I CAN EVEN SUGGEST A FIRST LINE FOR THE BOOK TO START YOU OUT ON THE LONG AND WINDING ROAD.
"MY NAME IS DARREN SHAN. I'VE ALWAYS BEEN FASCINATED..."
"...BY SPIDERS!"

IN THIS TIME, OF COURSE, I DO NOT KNOW YOU.
AND NOW THAT YOU HAVE REMOVED YOURSELF FROM YOUR ORIGINAL TIME LINE, I NEVER SHALL.
BUT I SENSE WE WERE FRIENDS.
GOOD LUCK TO YOU, FRIEND.
GOOD LUCK TO US ALL.
GACHA (CLICK)
NOW TO FIND A NICE QUIET SPOT WHERE I CAN BE ALONE...
...AND MAKE MY JOURNEY INTO THE BEYOND ...
YORO (WOBBLE)

HUFF!
HUFF!
I'LL GET HIM FOR THIS!!
YOU'LL PAY FOR THIS, CREEPY CREPS-LEY!!!
HOW DARE HE... CALL ME EVIL...
I'LL HAVE MY REVENGE!
GUSHI (RUB)
STEVE?
OH...
STEVE!? STEVE!!!

HAA (CHUFF)
HAA
HAA
DAR-REN...? WHY ARE YOU HERE?
YOU MEAN... YOU... SAW...?
GYU (SQUEEZE)
BA (LEAP)
I'M SORRY!! I'M SORRY, STEVE!!!
GABA (HUG)
I TRIE TO SAV YOU !!
BUT I THOUGHT YOU'D COME BACK, SO...
...I WAS WAITING HERE IN FRONT OF YOUR HOUSE...
I COULDN'T BELIEVE YOU WOULD STAY BEHIND IN THAT PLACE!!
BUT THEN SOME GUY IN A BLUE ROBE TOSSED ME OUT, AND I GOT AFRAID, AND I DIDN'T KNOW WHAT WAS GOING ON...
DARREN ...

THAT WASN'T FUNNY! IT WAS DANGER-OUS! DON'T DO STUFF LIKE THAT!!
WHAT IF I NEVER SAW YOU AGAIN!?
ARE WE FRIENDS OR NOT!?
WHAT ABOUT YOUR FRIENDS? YOU WOULD NOT BE ABLE TO SEE THEM AGAIN.
WHAT ABOUT YOUR PARENTS? WOULD YOU NOT MISS THE BOY YOU CAME WITH TONIGHT?
MY DAD DOESN'T LIVE WITH US, AND MY MOM DOESN'T LOVE ME.
SHE DOESN'T CARE WHAT I DO. SHE PROBABLY WON'T EVEN NOTICE I'M GONE.
YOU WOULD HAVE TO LEAVE SCHOOL AND HOME AND NEVER RETURN.
IT DOESN'T MATTER! I WANT TO BE A VAMPIRE MORE THAN I CARE ABOUT THEM!
BUT DARREN... YEAH, I GUESS IF I MISSED ANYONE, IT WOULD BE DARREN...

HIC!
SOB!
DARA (DRIP)
DARA
GUZU (SNUFFLE)
GUZU
WHOA...
UGH, GET OFF! YOU'RE WIPING SNOT ALL OVER ME!!
ACK!
GASA (SHUFF)
SHEESH... IT'S ALREADY MORNING.
HANG ON A SEC. I'LL GO TO MY ROOM AND GET MY SOCCER BALL.
LET'S GET TO SCHOOL EARLY, HAVE A MATCH, AND FORGET ABOUT THE CIRQUE DU FREAK...
OKAY, YEAH!!

IT ALL FEELS SO... PEACEFUL...
...FOR BEING MY SECOND DEATH...
BORO (CRUMBLE)
THERE IS NO PAIN...NO FEAR...NO LONELINESS...
BORO
I'VE DONE EVERYTHING... I NEEDED TO DO... I HAD ONE LAST LOOK AT MANY PEOPLE I LOVED...
DOSHA (SLUMP)
...BUT IT'S NOT AS THOUGH THERE'S NOTHING LEFT TO WORRY ABOUT.
BORO
DID MY OTHER SELF, THE YOUNGER ME... TRULY SAVE STEVE FROM HIS OWN EVENTUAL DESTRUCTION?
HA HA HA!
HA HA!
MY ONLY REGRET IS THAT I WON'T BE THERE...
...TO MAKE CERTAIN OF THAT...

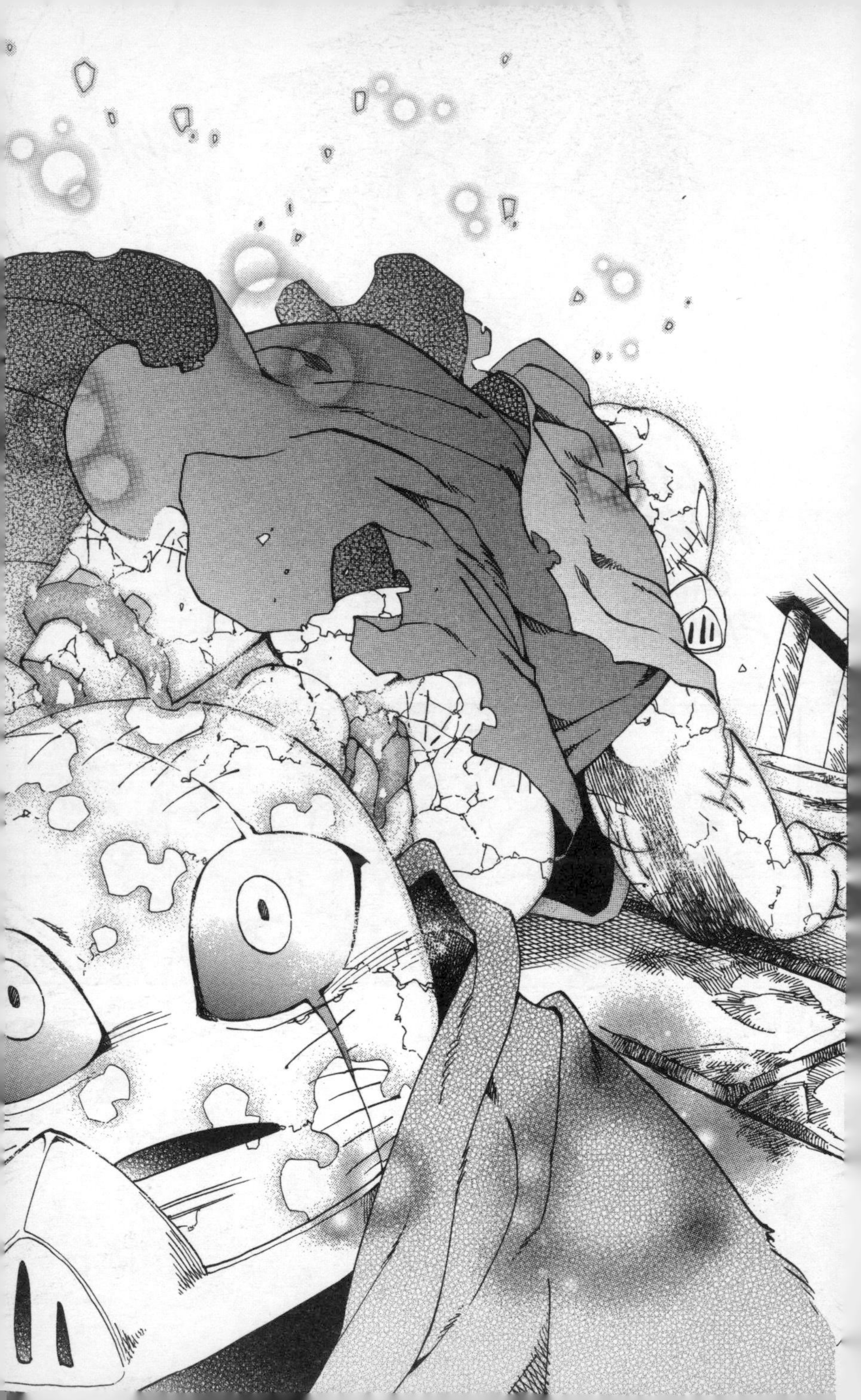

AHH...
IT'LL ALL TURN OUT FINE...
NO MATTER WHAT HAPPENS FROM THIS POINT ON...
...WE'LL BE FRIENDS ...
I'M LEAVING THE REST TO YOU...
...DARREN...
I HAVE TO GO NOW...

VOICES... I CAN HEAR VOICES ...
THE VOICES OF THOSE WAITING FOR ME IN THE GREAT BEYOND...
LAUGH-ING...

DARREN ...
LET'S GO!!
THE SAGA OF DARREN SHAN · THE END

THIS TWELFTH VOLUME OF THE DARREN SHAN MANGA MARKS THE END OF THE STORY, JUST AS THE TWELFTH NOVEL ENDED THE SERIES.

IT IS THANKS TO YOU READERS, WHO HAVE SUPPORTED THIS VENTURE FROM THE VERY BEGINNING, THAT WE ARE BOTH HERE AT THIS EPILOGUE RIGHT NOW. THANK YOU!!

THROUGHOUT THIS SERIES, I WORKED UNDER A VERY HARSH, DIFFICULT CONDITION: CRAMMING ONE NOVEL INTO A SINGLE VOLUME OF MANGA.
I FELT TONS OF PRESSURE TO SOMEHOW GET ACROSS THE BEST ELEMENTS OF THE ORIGINAL STORIES INTO EACH VOLUME...
HII
HII (WHEEZE)
BUT LOOKING BACK NOW, THE PRESSURE WAS EASILY OUTWEIGHED BY THE JOY OF REPRESENTING THE WORLD AND CHARACTERS OF DARREN SHAN.
THIS IS FUN!!
DRAWING THE FINAL CHAPTER WAS A CONFLICTING EXPERIENCE. IT WAS LIKE I WAS SAYING GOOD-BYE TO MY OWN TEACHER AND FRIENDS.
HUFF
HUFF

THANKS ARE IN ORDER TO MY STAFF AND THEIR HELP IN KEEPING ME ON DEADLINE: JUNYA, A-KUN, T-KUN.
ISHIHARA-SAN AND KANZAKI-SAN, MY EDITORS OVER THE COURSE OF THE SERIES.
HASHIMOTO-SAN THE TRANSLATOR AND TAGUCHI-SAN THE ILLUSTRATOR OF THE ORIGINAL NOVELS, WHO WERE A HUGE INFLUENCE ON MY VERSION OF THE SERIES.
GARI (SCRITCH)
GARI
THE SHONEN SUNDAY EDITORIAL STAFF, WHO HELPED ME VISIT LONDON AND HOLLYWOOD, AS WELL AS BOOK SIGNINGS AND OTHER EVENTS.
MY CARING AND COMPASSIONATE READERS, WHO CHEERED AN AMATEUR ARTIST WITH THEIR LETTERS AND E-MAILS.
BOOK: DARREN SHAN XII
AND OF COURSE, THE CREATOR OF THIS WORLD...
...FOR HIS FANTASTIC AND MOVING STORY, DARREN-SAN!
TO EVERY-ONE WHO PLAYED A PART IN THE MANGA DARREN SHAN...
...NOTHING BUT THE HIGHEST GRATITUDE FROM MY ENTIRE HEART!!!

THIS MARKS THE END OF THE DARREN SHAN MANGA, BUT THIS ADAPTATION OF THE STORY IS JUST ONE POSSIBLE VISION OF THE FULL SERIES.
BY READING THE ORIGINAL NOVELS, YOU'LL SEE PIECES OF THE STORY AND FASCINATING DETAILS THAT COULDN'T FIT INTO A COMIC BOOK AND BROADEN YOUR VISION OF THE WORLD OF DARREN SHAN. EACH ADAPTATION OFFERS A DIFFERENT TAKE ON THE STORY!!
I'LL BE DREAMING OF THE DAY WE MEET AGAIN...
ありがとうございました!!
THANK YOU SO MUCH!!

I HOPE AND PRAY THAT THIS MANGA ONLY ADDS TO YOUR EXPERIENCE EXPLORING THE WORLD OF DARREN SHAN.

TH… ⑫

So…

Darren Shan
Takahiro Arai

…ished in Japan in 2009 by Shogakukan Inc., Tokyo.
…ghts in the UK and The Commonwealth arranged with
Shogakukan Inc. through Tuttle-Mori Agency, Inc., Tokyo.

Published in Great Britain by HarperCollins *Children's Books* in 2012
HarperCollins *Children's Books* is a division of HarperCollins*Publishers* Ltd,
77–85 Fulham Palace Road, Hammersmith, London, W6 8JB.

The HarperCollins website address is
www.harpercollins.co.uk

ISBN: 978-0-00-750646-0

Printed and bound in England by Clays Ltd, St Ives plc

FSC™ is a non-profit international organisation established to promote the responsible management of the world's forests. Products carrying the FSC label are independently certified to assure consumers that they come from forests that are managed to meet the social, economic and ecological needs of present and future generations, and other controlled sources.

Find out more about HarperCollins and the environment at
www.harpercollins.co.uk/green